DCHewett

SCHOLASTI

C000156284

MATHS

KEY STAGE 2

SCOTTISH LEVELS C-E

ASSESSMENT

IAN GARDNER & JEAN EDWARDS

Published by Scholastic Ltd,
Villiers House,
Clarendon Avenue,
Leamington Spa,
Warwickshire CV32 5PR

© 1998 Scholastic Ltd
2 3 4 5 6 7 8 9 0   9 0 1 2 3 4 5 6 7

Authors
Ian Gardner and Jean Edwards

Editor
Joel Lane

Series Design
Joy White

Designer
Anna Oliwa

Illustration
Ray and Corinne Burrows

Designed using Adobe Pagemaker

British Library Cataloguing-in-Publication Data
A catalogue record for this book is available from the British Library

ISBN 0-590-53641-9

The rights of Ian Gardner and Jean Edwards to be
identified as the Author of this Work have
been asserted by them in accordance with the
Copyright, Designs and Patents Act 1988.

All rights reserved. This book is sold subject to the condition that it shall not, by way of
trade or otherwise, be lent, hired out or otherwise circulated without the publisher's
prior consent in any form of binding or cover other than that in which it is published
and without a similar condition, including this condition, being imposed upon the
subsequent purchaser.

No part of this publication may be reproduced, stored in a retrieval system, or
transmitted, in any form or by any means, electronic, mechanical, photocopying,
recording or otherwise, without the prior permission of the publisher. This book remains
copyright, although permission is granted to copy pages 13–14, 44–118, 124–136,
146–166 and 174–188 for classroom distribution and use only in the school which
has purchased the book, or by the teacher who has purchased the book, and in
accordance with the CLA licensing agreement. Photocopying permission is given for
purchasers only and not for borrowers of the book from any lending service.

CONTENTS

MEASURING   167

INTRODUCTION

ABOUT PORTFOLIO ASSESSMENT

Assessment is something that teachers do all the time. It is an integral part of the process of teaching. While much of it goes unrecorded, teachers nevertheless continually formulate judgements based on their observations of children working.

The term 'portfolio assessment' refers to planned interventions that allow the child to demonstrate what he/she knows and can do. Unlike standardised tasks and tests, however, portfolio assessment focuses on qualitative judgements of performance. Although as a teacher you may wish to relate these evaluations to national norms, the objective of such tasks is not to give a percentage, score or grade. The outcomes themselves, recorded by the teacher and/or the child, constitute the evidence. This evidence should not only indicate what the child has achieved, it should also provide pointers as to what knowledge and skills are required for the child to move forward.

The fostering of mathematical capability requires both attention to the way we present the subject and an appreciation that every child learns in a unique way. Portfolio assessment encourages these perspectives by placing the onus on teachers to use professional judgements in presenting and adapting the tasks to suit individual needs. Incorporated as another facet in the practice of teaching, portfolio assessment offers a series of reference points by which to judge the learner. It can also provide valuable feedback to inform future approaches to teaching by highlighting those steps that have proved particularly effective in moving the child's learning forward.

THE CONCEPT OF AN ASSESSMENT PORTFOLIO

Portfolios come in a great variety of formats, and can have different functions for various professions. Compare, for example, the purpose of an artist's portfolio with that of one developed for financial investment. In educational terms, a portfolio is viewed as a window through which we can gain an insight into the individual's developing capability. It is a selection of dated samples of work, illustrating or providing examples of significant performance in a range of contexts and in different areas of a subject. Supported by brief annotations and contextual information from the teacher, the portfolio can provide a measure both of the child's strengths and of those aspects in need of further development.

FUNCTIONS OF THE ASSESSMENT PORTFOLIO

The two main functions of this portfolio are diagnostic and celebratory. In its diagnostic function, the assessment portfolio informs teachers' decisions about the learning environment and about individual children's needs. Assessing what the child knows and how well he/she responds to the experiences presented allows the teacher to make sensitive and informed decisions about future learning steps. By asking probing questions, by closely observing the child's interactions with others, and by analysing recorded outcomes, we can approach a more exact sense of where individual strengths and weaknesses lie.

The diagnostic function

The power of diagnostic assessment lies not in specifying how one child can be judged in relation to another, but in identifying what makes that child's awareness unique. As the teacher gains more information about this awareness, he/she becomes able to fine-tune the teaching to match the needs of the child more precisely. Thus feedback leads to 'feed-forward'; an ongoing cycle of teaching, assessing and reviewing is established.

Parents may benefit from the diagnostic information you offer them. It is important that such dialogue clearly identifies perceived areas of strength and weakness, and clarifies the mutual responsibilities involved in moving the child's learning forward. In reporting to parents, many schools have found that setting specific goals helps to focus attention on these points.

The celebratory function

The second important function of the assessment portfolio is to document the child's achievements. We should not underestimate the importance of incorporating the learner in this process, as there is arguably no better motivating force than evidence of one's own progress. As teachers, we use this information to gain a specific knowledge of where along the continuum of mathematical development the child lies. The detailed evidence, together with earlier samples of work for comparison, can give valuable indications regarding the rate at which progress is being made. The portfolio will enhance the sharing of information in both interviews and written reports.

On a broader front, the portfolio also gives the teacher things to celebrate as groups of children progress over an extended period of time. In observing the children's progress, the teacher can begin to identify those interventions and teaching programmes which have been particularly effective, and gain a heightened sense of her/his continued professional development.

SCHOLASTIC PORTFOLIO ASSESSMENT AND MATHEMATICAL ASSESSMENT

Assessment in mathematics focuses not only on the child's learned knowledge and skills, but also on the child's ability to apply that learning. Unlike some more formalised approaches to assessment, the portfolio approach aims to be genuinely diagnostic: it highlights particular strengths and misconceptions. This is achieved in many of the activities by presenting tasks which allow for a variety of responses. By opting for a relatively open approach, the teacher is well-placed to identify significant features of an individual's work and to act on that information:

Plan the assessment activity
↓
Conduct the activity and collect information
↓
Review the information gathered
↓
Plan further activity based on the above

The teacher's role in this process is fundamental – both in preparing and managing the learning environment and in taking opportunities to observe, listen, discuss, question, extend and intervene.

Significant assessment possibilities often arise when an unfamiliar problem requires resolution. The activities in *Scholastic Portfolio Assessment* require the child both to draw on their knowledge, skills and understanding and to use and apply them in new ways. This ability to use and apply mathematics lies at the heart of the subject, and is the element that truly means the child is working mathematically.

Towards a whole-school approach

Scholastic Portfolio Assessment lends itself readily to use as the framework for a whole-school approach to maths assessment. Used by the whole school, the activities can provide evidence of continuity and progression across Key

Stage 2 (P4 to P7) years. It will be important for a school to make some decisions about which activities are appropriate for each year group, in order to prevent inappropriate repetition. Some activities would be appropriate to repeat in successive years as the child progresses. Teachers could also benefit from sharing pieces of work and reaching a consensus on what the outcomes indicate about a child's achievements.

A portfolio offers benefits for the child and the parent or carer as well. It establishes a dialogue with the child which can be an important early step in active learning. If the child shares in the assessment of her/his progress, she/he gains a broader awareness of expectations and an opportunity to understand what constitutes significant evidence. This can have a motivational benefit, particularly for the child who is anxious or suffers from low self-esteem. Parents also value the opportunity to engage in the learning process. Samples of work constitute a tangible outcome to be shared. An evaluation of such work can lead to a better understanding of the individual's strengths and areas for further development. Portfolio assessment thus has scope for target setting.

In relation to individual pupils, *Scholastic Portfolio Assessment* offers:
* feedback on teaching;
* detailed evidence of progress made over the short and the long term;
* insights into the child's ability to apply her/his learning;
* a bank of evidence to support summative judgements of attainment;
* appraisal of a balance of skills and knowledge;
* insights into the future learning needs of the child.

Used more broadly, it can support a group of teachers in a school by:
* establishing broad judgements of the progress and attainment made by the children in a year group;
* providing feedback on the breadth of curricular provision;
* encouraging a consensus judgement of performance;
* focusing attention on equal opportunity issues in relation to the progress made by different groups;
* drawing attention to the range of teaching and learning styles.

Use and management of the assessment portfolio

The *Scholastic Portfolio Assessment* series covers mathematics, literacy and science. The two mathematics titles offer focused guidance on all areas of the mathematics curriculum. They have been developed to cover relevant parts of the National Curriculum Programmes of Study for England and Wales, the Scottish 5–14 Guidelines and the Northern Ireland Curriculum. They are designed to be used in a flexible way: it is not necessary to follow any specific page order, or to use all of the photocopiable pages. These books give teachers the means to assess key skills and knowledge at whatever times suit their own and the children's needs.

We strongly recommend that the themes presented in this book are integrated into your teaching so that the child comes to each assessment task with some prior experience of the ideas and conventions involved. This then allows a judgement to be made of how well the child is able to apply the experience in a new context. Some of the tasks identify whether skills can be carried through; others confirm the extent of the child's understanding.

The resources in this book are aimed at teachers of children at Key Stage 2 (Primary 4–7). A companion volume in this series covers the assessment of mathematics at Key Stage 1 (Primary 1–3). The content coverage in this book consists of four chapters: Number (including money and algebra); Handling data; Shape and space; and Measures. Each of these chapters contains:

- **Background information.** This sets out the rationale for the content of the chapter and, in some instances, gives technical advice and background information (for example, on differentiating the assessment of shape from that of number).
- **Teachers' notes.** Although some guidance is detailed on each photocopiable sheet, more comprehensive notes are given here on the conduct and administration of the task. These notes also detail some of the different outcomes that might be expected from children of different ages, abilities and levels of prior experience.
- **Photocopiable assessment sheets.** The left-hand margin of each sheet gives brief notes on the assessment focus, the relevant skills in using and applying mathematics and the nature of the task, along with some assessment pointers. This is convenient for working with the child, and also serves as a reminder at a later date when the portfolio is viewed retrospectively. The remainder of the page presents the activity and acts as a record of the child's work. In some instances, that record will be supported by additions and entries made by the teacher. Many of the sheets are ready to photocopy; others require the addition of a few numbers or words appropriate to the needs of the child.

Use and application of mathematics

You may note from the content coverage outlined above that the child's ability to use and apply mathematics is not detailed within a separate chapter. This important element is integrated throughout the activities. The focus within each activity depends on the nature of the task. In broad terms, the following elements feature: explaining and reasoning; talking about the work; asking and answering questions; selecting materials and mathematics; presenting work in different ways; working in a systematic and organised way; identifying patterns; making predictions; drawing conclusions; and making general statements.

Specific references to using and applying mathematics skills are given on the photocopiable sheets, in the teachers' notes, and in the curriculum charts on pages 13–14 and 189–192. The charts comprise a listing of the book's coverage of the National Curriculum for England and Wales, and links to the Northern Ireland Curriculum and the Scottish 5–14 Guidelines.

When and how to use the assessments

It would be unrealistic to give definite age recommendations for these activities, for several reasons. Firstly, many of the challenges give opportunities for work at various levels of capability, and could justifiably be used two or three times by the same child. A young child, for example, may explore a task at a simple level and record in a way that refers to the objects being handled. With support, there may be scope for discussion, pictorial representation and the opportunity to follow a set of instructions. A child with more experience of the ideas under scrutiny may show greater independence, record symbolically and begin to ask questions of her/his own. An older or able child may make decisions for her/himself and find ways to overcome difficulties encountered along the way. In some cases, the child may begin to make general statements and talk in mathematical terms without ambiguity.

Another reason for not assigning activities by pupil age is that situational factors can have a significant effect on the level of skills and knowledge that a child brings on entry to school. Furthermore, the composition of teaching groups varies widely (sometimes involving a wide age span); and thus it would be unrealistic to expect all the children to undertake the same activities routinely.

Before using the sheets with children, you will need to familiarise yourself with the purpose and conduct of each assessment in order to make any necessary changes to the sheet before photocopying and to gather any additional resources that are required. The sequence in which you use the sheets should be appropriate to the needs of the children. Within each chapter, there are several sections. Within the chapter on 'Number, money and algebra', for example, there is a section dealing with addition. Each section contains what we consider to be a progression of activities, arranged broadly in order of increasing difficulty. This is only a guide, however, and you may well use them in a different order or miss some out altogether. Some activities may be used once and then modified on a future occasion, while others may be inappropriate for your class.

Completed *Scholastic Portfolio Assessment* sheets can be integrated with other ongoing work (from workbooks or folders) to generate a portfolio. Only samples which represent significant or representative achievement should be retained in this way.

The word 'assessment' sometimes conjures up images of a highly formal process. It is important to provide an environment which allays any such anxieties, and to establish work on the portfolio as just another of the classroom routines. In contrast to a typical lesson, however, it is anticipated that the child will be building on skills and ideas that have already been explored on a previous occasion. In some cases, it will be necessary to clarify why the task is being undertaken, and to share the assessment objectives of the task with the child. If the task proves too difficult for the child, it will be appropriate to offer support or to modify the activity. In some circumstances you may even opt to discontinue the task, though this should be avoided if possible as it can lead to a sense of failure. When support is given, it is good practice to annotate or code the child's work to act as a reminder that some additional teaching has taken place. It may be helpful to tell the child what you are writing, in order to maintain openness and mutual trust.

Most teachers will want to select activities which link to work that has taken place recently in the classroom. Before the child begins a task, you should make sure that he/she understands what the task involves. Encourage the child to ask for help if he/she is puzzled. When the child has finished, promote reflection by talking about the work. Offer some immediate constructive feedback so that the child can begin the process of self-evaluation. It is vital that, in doing mathematical work of this nature, the child is not left unhappy or confused. Pupil self-evaluation and teacher evaluation of the activities can be assisted by the use of photocopiable pages 13 and 14.

FURTHER READING
The chapter on Assessment in the Primary Professional Bookshelf title *Teaching Numeracy*, edited by Ruth Merttens (Scholastic, 1997), provides a useful background to the themes discussed in this Introduction.

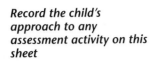

Name _____ *Date* _____

Pupil analysis sheet

Teachers' notes, page 12

Record the child's approach to any assessment activity on this sheet

Teacher comments:

Length of activity

Short (under 20 minutes) ☐

Medium (20-40 minutes) ☐

Long (over 40 minutes) ☐

Is the activity:

◆ divided up into many short tasks? ☐

◆ divided up into longer, more substantial tasks? ☐

◆ one, holistic task? ☐

Main content objective

Note the PoS statements and AT levels that pupil working within

Number and algebra	Measures	Shape	Handling data

Process objectives (tick as appropriate)

Selection of materials/mathematics ☐

Communication of ideas ☐

Generalising ☐

_____ ☐

_____ ☐

_____ ☐

Other issues (brief comments)

Concentration _____

Independence _____

Understanding _____

Support _____

Any other comments

Mathematics review sheet

Allows self-evaluation by the child of any mathematical activity.

Allow the child time for self-evaluation before discussing his or her responses on the sheet.

Activity content:

Teacher's comments

What did you use?

Who did you work with?

_____

_____

_____

How hard was it?

Easy	OK	A bit hard	Very hard

Did you like it?

A lot	A bit	OK	Not much	Not at all

Teachers' notes, page 12

This grid indicates links between the activities and the relevant sections of the Programme of Study for Mathematics at Key Stage 2. For each activity, reference is made to links with 'Using and applying mathematics' and the appropriate content areas.

NATIONAL CURRICULUM FOR MATHEMATICS (ENGLAND AND WALES)

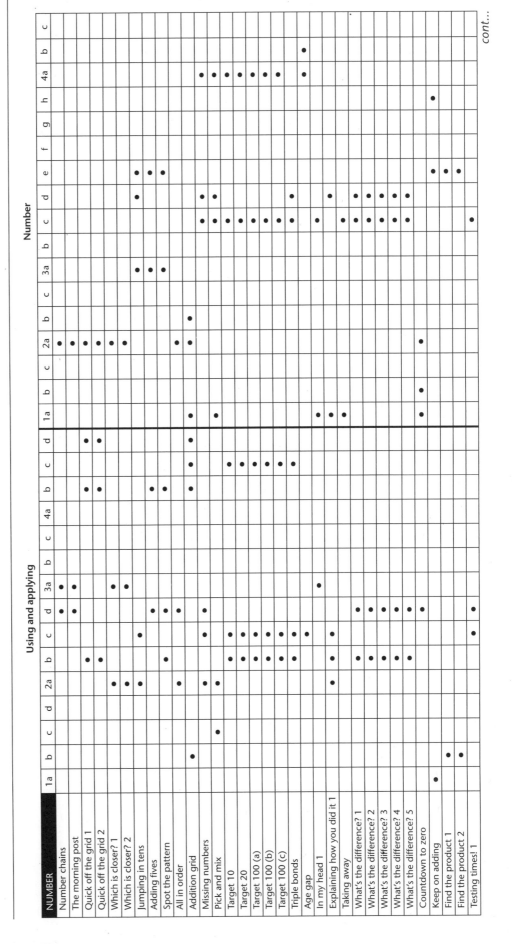

The chart is a grid of activity links. The column groupings are **Using and applying** (columns 1a, b, c, d, 2a, b, c, d, 3a, b, c, d, 4a, b, c, d) and **Number** (columns 1a, b, c, 2a, b, c, 3a, b, c, d, e, f, g, h, 4a, b, c).

The **NUMBER** activity rows are:

- Number chains
- The morning post
- Quick off the grid 1
- Quick off the grid 2
- Which is closer? 1
- Which is closer? 2
- Jumping in tens
- Adding fives
- Spot the pattern
- All in order
- Addition grid
- Missing numbers
- Pick and mix
- Target 10
- Target 20
- Target 100 (a)
- Target 100 (b)
- Target 100 (c)
- Triple bonds
- Age gap
- In my head 1
- Explaining how you did it 1
- Taking away
- What's the difference? 1
- What's the difference? 2
- What's the difference? 3
- What's the difference? 4
- What's the difference? 5
- Countdown to zero
- Keep on adding
- Find the product 1
- Find the product 2
- Testing times! 1

cont...

Using and applying | **Number**

NUMBER	| 1a	b	c	d	2a	b	c	d	3a	b	c	4a	b	c	d	|| 1a	b	c	2a	b	c	3a	b	c	d	e	f	g	h	4a	b	c
Testing times! 2			●	●												●		●															
Testing times! 3			●	●												●		●															
Number bugs					●								●									●	●										
Perfect bugs					●																	●	●								●		
Puzzling times						●	●								●																		
Square numbers 1									●	●				●				●															
Square numbers 2					●		●		●	●				●				●				●	●										
Cube numbers					●													●															
Keep on taking away																●													●				
Mix and match						●	●									●																	
Explaining how you did it 2																																	
Division One		●			●																												
Premier Division		●			●																												
Find four facts						●							●					●															
Fill in the gaps									●					●		●		●					●										
In my head 2					●				●	●								●						●			●	●					
In my head 3					●				●									●						●			●	●	●				
Blank cheques 1	●																			●	●												
Blank cheques 2	●																			●													
European survey					●					●						●																	
Below zero	●																																
Real numbers	●	●				●										●				●		●											
Fractions 1		●			●																	●		●									
Fractions 2		●			●		●				●											●		●									
Fractions 3		●			●																			●									
Fractions 4					●																			●									
Percentages				●																			●							●			
Spot the pattern						●	●																●							●			
What did I do?						●									●	●							●			●						●	
What comes later?												●	●		●	●							●								●	●	
Spot the rule												●											●			●							
Double trouble			●								●												●										
Input, output 1										●			●						●					●									●

cont...

cont...

NUMBER

Using and applying | Number

NUMBER	1a	b	c	d	2a	b	c	3a	d	c	b	4a	c	d		1a	b	c	2a	b	3a	b	c	d	4a	b	c	d	e	f	g	h	4a	b	c
Input, output 2				•	•															•					•										
Input, output 3				•	•													•		•					•										
Trampoline party	•					•	•																		•										
A sound deal							•			•															•										
Shopper's choice					•					•															•										
Find it!											•										•				•										
Round the block							•	•													•				•						•				
Nearest numbers					•			•											•														•	•	•
Hundreds and thousands	•						•									•																			

DATA HANDLING

Using and applying | Handling data

DATA HANDLING	1a	b	c	d	2a	b	c	3a	b	c	4a	b	c	d		1a	b	c	2a	b	c	3a	b	c	d
Watching TV		•			•											•			•	•					
Yes or no?		•														•			•	•					
My own chart		•	•													•	•		•	•					
What colour is your car?							•						•	•					•						
Pocket money					•	•											•								
Pie chart					•								•						•	•	•				
Averages				•														•							
Computer database		•		•		•												•					•		
Possibly, maybe		•						•														•			
How likely?		•						•														•	•		
What's the chance?		•						•														•		•	
In the bag								•				•	•				•					•		•	•
Two coins		•						•				•	•				•					•		•	•

SHAPE AND SPACE

Using and applying | Shape, space and measures

SHAPE AND SPACE	1a	b	c	d	2a	b	c	3a	b	c	4a	b	c	d		1a	b	c	2a	b	c	3a	b	c	4a	b	c
2D shapes	•							•											•			•					
Sort the shapes 1								•								•			•			•					
Drawing straws								•									•							•			
What's it called?								•											•								
True or false?		•														•					•						
3D shapes								•						•		•			•								•
Sort the shapes 2								•								•			•			•		•			

SHAPE AND SPACE

	Using and applying													Shape, space and measures													
	1a	b	c	d	2a	b	3a	b	c	4a	b	c	d	1a	b	c	d	e	2a	b	c	3a	b	c	4a	b	c
Shape designs							●												●								
What's in a name?	●				●		●					●		●					●								
Describe the shapes	●						●				●			●					●								
Draw the shape	●				●		●							●					●								
Mirror symmetry					●		●													●	●	●					
Lines of symmetry	●							●							●		●			●	●	●					
Rotational symmetry	●																●		●		●	●					
Angle 1		●			●						●	●	●											●			
Angle 2		●									●	●	●			●								●			
Angle 3		●			●						●	●	●			●								●			
Nets of shapes					●											●			●								
Area and perimeter		●							●		●	●				●									●	●	●
Same area, different shape			●																	●							●
Enlargement								●				●											●				●

MEASURING

	Using and applying													Shape, space and measures													
	1a	b	c	d	2a	b	3a	b	c	4a	b	c	d	1a	b	c	d	e	2a	b	c	3a	b	c	4a	b	c
How do you measure it?	●				●									●					●								
How long are your leaves?	●				●							●		●					●						●	●	
Measuring around	●				●							●		●					●						●	●	●
Circles		●							●		●					●		●									
Scale drawing		●						●							●			●									
Surface area		●										●								●							
Volume and surface area		●										●								●							
How much is in the jug?	●																	●							●		
What order?						●																			●		
Weighing out the potatoes	●											●													●		
Is it true?																									●		
Which is greater?	●					●																			●		
Catching the bus	●												●												●	●	
Catching the train	●												●												●	●	
Time to investigate	●							●																	●		

SCHOLASTIC
Portfolio
ASSESSMENT

NUMBER

NUMBER (INCLUDING ALGEBRA AND MONEY)

The activities in this chapter cover the development of awareness in number, money and algebra through Key Stage 2 (Primary 4–7). They address the following areas:
- work with large numbers;
- the four operations (×, ÷, + and –);
- negative numbers;
- fractions, percentages and decimals;
- money;
- number patterns and relationships;
- multiplication and division facts;
- number properties (for example, prime numbers);
- mental methods;
- use of calculators.

The development of skills and understanding in number is a complex process, unique to each child. The interrelatedness of number activities makes it unrealistic to consider the above list simply as a checklist of discrete items. Consider how mental methods, for example, feature in the majority of mathematical processes; while specific activities in this chapter address mental calculation, it should also be routinely discussed in order to keep children's awareness of it in full view.

In broad terms, this chapter deals with number, money and algebra from the following perspectives:
- developing an understanding of place value and extending awareness of numbers to very large, fractional and negative numbers;
- understanding relationships between numbers and developing methods of computation;
- solving numerical problems.

PLACE VALUE AND THE NUMBER SYSTEM

The work on place value in this chapter builds on ideas that the child will typically have encountered at an earlier stage. Although the child may already have worked with larger numbers, the significance of place value may not be fully appreciated. Explicit understanding of the decimal number system becomes more important when decimal fractions are introduced. Without a sound basis of understanding, there is considerable scope for misconceptions such as:
- 'the longer a number is, the bigger it is'
  eg 1.2567 > 2.3
- 'if you multiply by ten, you just add 0'
  eg 1.2 × 10 = 1.20
- the parts of a number are written in sequences, as they are spoken
  eg 'one thousand and sixty-eight' is written 100068

Money and measurement

To some extent, the child makes use of decimal fractions in the context of money and measurement. Nevertheless, a sense of positional value is still required to recognise, for example, that £10.06 and not £10.6 is the correct representation of ten pounds and six pence. This awareness is also necessary for calculator work in these contexts. Unless the calculator has a facility to 'fix' the number of decimal places, it will disregard a 0 where this has no value as a place holder. The calculation of £3.60 ÷ 2, for example, gives a result of 1.8, which in turn requires interpretation to be converted back into the context of money (£1.80). This point is made explicitly in the Scottish Guidelines (Level C).

Percentages

Some activities in this chapter assess the child's understanding of percentages. In particular, the relationship between percentages and their fractional equivalents is addressed. The focus of these tasks move towards the recognition of a percentage as a fractional part of a quantity, not just as a part of a unit whole.

RELATIONSHIPS BETWEEN NUMBERS

Although the younger child will already have encountered patterns and sequences, Key Stage 2 involves a stronger focus on the generalisability of number, providing the basis for later work on algebra.

Patterns

Pattern recognition is assessed extensively in this chapter. Initially it is anticipated that the child will appreciate the idea of a numerical pattern: a sequence that is guided by a generating rule. For example, the sequence 2, 4, 6, 8... has the generating rule 'Add two to find the next number in the sequence.'

If the child is able to copy and continue patterns, he/she may then go on to create further patterns using different generating rules. For the child's understanding to move forward, he/she needs to develop an ability to predict for a term much further along the sequence. For example, in the sequence beginning 3, 4, 5... the hundredth term will be 102. At this point, the child moves on to describing an observed rule for prediction in her/his or her own words. At the upper end of attainment (Year 6/P7), a child may be able to describe such a rule in abstract terms. Thus in the example above, the nth term will have a value of n + 2.

Familiar number sequences

Some specific number sequences (such as square numbers) are assessed in this chapter, with the properties of these numbers receiving close scrutiny. The multiplication facts will be a familiar sequence to children and adults alike. Specific activities allow you to judge both the child's knowledge of the number sequences and the extent of his/her recall.

DEVELOPING METHODS OF CALCULATION

The assessments in this chapter which relate to the calculation of conventional number problems ('sums') are based on three fundamental principles:
• The child should be encouraged to find solutions in her/his way. In doing so, significant assessment evidence can be gathered.
• The child should be exposed to efficient methods of calculation.
• No one method of calculation is universally the most efficient. The best algorithm (a set routine or sequence of operations to solve a problem) often depends on the numbers involved.

Solving numerical problems

Although it is not important that the child should be assessed on her/his ability to do conventional 'sums', it is essential that tasks can be accessed by the child when they are embedded in a context. This chapter features several activities of this kind; some of them relate to number 'problems', while others deal with 'realistic' contexts. Although the difference is subtle, the latter are essential if the child is genuinely to become an independent mathematician. If too much reliance is placed on contrived mathematical word problems, it becomes easy for the child to carry out such tasks based on the nature of the preceding work (for example, practice in subtraction). It is only by placing the child in a truly unstructured situation (such as costing for a class tea party) that a full judgement can be made of her/his competence. In particular, the activities offer opportunities to assess the child's applied knowledge of mathematics in situations involving money and measurement.

The subject demands at this stage should not be underestimated. A 10- to 11-year-old may be able to engage in aspects of mathematics at a level that would challenge most adults. To support the busy teacher, comprehensive teaching notes are provided with these activities; where appropriate, solutions are included.

TEACHING NOTES FOR INDIVIDUAL ACTIVITIES

Number chains
page 44

Counting on and back in equal sets from a given number Prepare the chains of numbers you are going to use for each group or the class. This will involve deciding how to limit the range; you may wish to return to the same sheet at intervals, extending the numbers you start and end with each time. Try to make sure that you include chains of numbers low in the range, such as 104 to 113 and 196 to 205, to give you an opportunity to check that the child can go over the hundred.

When the child has finished, look at her/his errors (if any) to assess whether there are any areas of misunderstanding that need further work. Some children might find the crossover from one group of hundreds to the next confusing, or find counting backwards more difficult than counting forwards. For more confident children who complete this task easily, you might move on to four-figure numbers. In this case, it would be advisable to enlarge the boxes on the sheet.

The morning post
page 45

Ordering three-digit numbers Prepare four sets of five envelopes with addresses, including house numbers. Make sure that the house numbers are at least three digits and cover the range you are intending to assess. In order to provide a more realistic context, the numbers could refer to flats in a tower block; or, as an extension, the group could sort the envelopes into odd-number and reverse even-number sequences (or vice versa) for delivery to houses in a street. You may wish to provide differentiation between groups by choosing numbers from 100 to 200, numbers from 100 to 1000, or numbers that require very close reading to be ordered (such as 104, 140, 401 and 144). If you do this, it would be wise to make each group's envelopes a different colour in case they get mixed up.

When the child has finished, look carefully at any mistakes he/she has made. It might be that the child is more confident with numbers earlier in the range, or that the child can work confidently with numbers that are clearly different but finds numbers with the same digits in different places more confusing.

Quick off the grid 1
and 2
pages 46 and 47

Counting on and back within 100 and beyond 100 (respectively) You may wish to alter the complexity of these assessment tasks by either adding additional numbers or removing some before photocopying the grids. (If numbers are removed, you will need to make sure that enough numbers remain to allow completion of the task.) These activities should be conducted without access to visual cues such as number grids and calculators. While there is no 'right way' to work through the tasks, it is important that, wherever possible, the assessment is completed without support. Talk to the child about the strategies he/she is using to fill in the missing numbers.

The arrangements of the numbers are not always immediately obvious, and you should observe and judge the child's ability to persevere. On the first sheet, the numbers are arranged: in 2s, left to right along each row moving down the grid; back in 1s down the columns, moving from left to right; back in 3s, left to right along the rows moving down the grid. On the second sheet, the numbers are arranged: in 2s from right to left along each row, moving up the grid; in 1s from left to right along each row, moving up the grid; across in 5s from left to right, going down the grid.

Counting on and back are skills which some children find difficult; some children, for example, need a 'run up' to the number before counting on. You should assess whether the child's familiarity with number sequences enables her/him to fill in the gaps in the sequences. The final grid in 'Quick off the grid 2' takes the child beyond 100; at this stage, you should expect due attention to place value (eg 101 not 1001).

Which is closer?
1 and 2
pages 48 and 49

Rounding up and down to the nearest 10 or 100 The child is effectively being asked to round the middle number up or down to the nearest ten or hundred. It will be important to observe or ask the child how he/she works out the answers. You may wish to make a note of the methods used on the sheet. Some children will work mentally; less confident or younger children may need a number line to confirm their answers.

(Sheet 1 should be completed first, and should be straightforward for most children in Key Stage 2 (Primary 4–7), allowing a quick check of their prior learning. On sheet 2, you could extend the more able child by asking him/her to record how much closer the nearer number is when he/she is rounding up or down. The child might express this by saying, for instance, that is closer by 20 to 600 than to 700, or by saying that the difference between 640 and 600 is 40 whereas the difference between 640 and 700 is 60.

Jumping in tens
page 50

Counting in tens This task assesses the child's ability to count in tens (forwards and/or backwards) from a given three-figure number using her/his understanding of place value. Before photocopying the sheet, decide the range of numbers you are going to work with. For Year 3 and 4 (P4 and P5) children, you might use numbers from 0 to 500; for Year 5 and 6 (P6 and P7) children, you might use numbers to 1000. You should include a sequence that starts just before going over a hundred (eg at 286). You might also expect older children to count in any size of step from/to any number, including numbers beyond 1000 and negative numbers. You could ask the child to attempt this extension work on the reverse of the sheet.

The child should be encouraged to use mental methods to work out the number of jumps. Some children might record the steps (by tallying or drawing) in order to remember them. The child should write out one complete sequence so that you can check the steps and the child's ability to record three-digit numbers.

Adding fives
page 51

Identifying and applying a number pattern This task should give you the opportunity to find out more about the child's ability to spot patterns, generalise, predict and check predictions. A child who is confident with these skills should be able to base predictions on experience of the previous patterns, and to make the connection that the pairs of numbers are 5 apart each time (so 2 must be paired with 7, and 4 with 9). He/she should recognise that the units column produces a simple repeating pattern (of alternating digits) in each case.

Spot the pattern
page 52

Identifying and developing a number pattern The child should be familiar with the units pattern in the 5 times table before working on this investigation. You might look at the 5 times pattern with the group or class as an introduction to this task. The child could be provided with a calculator to check a later part of the pattern where mentally adding on is more difficult or time-consuming.

The child should look for and isolate the recurring pattern and be able to show one complete section of it (for example, in the 3 times table, it is 3 6 9 2 5 8 1 4 7 0). You might direct individual children to particular times tables linked to their ability or interest level, or try them on the 2 times table and then ask them to attempt a more difficult one on the back of the sheet. The child may notice patterns that can be helpful in memorising multiplication facts or using mental recall more effectively – for example, in the 9 times table the units pattern goes down in ones.

The child's ability to find the segment of pattern that recurs, and to check or demonstrate that it does recur, will indicate her/his understanding of repeating patterns. The clarity and accuracy of the child's explanation of what he/she has found and her/his ability to make further connections between patterns will indicate a more sophisticated understanding. For example, a child may explore the 3 pattern, finding 3 6 9 2 5 8 1 4 7 0, then explore the 6 pattern, finding 6 2 8 4 0, then make and explain the connection (every other number, because 6 is twice 3).

All in order
page 53

Ordering numbers to 1000 Different digits could be provided for each child to individualise the assessment. While the child is working through the activity, ask her/him to read the numbers aloud to you. You should also observe how systematically the child is working through the task.

The principal focus for this assessment is the ability to order numbers. If the activity proves to be problematic, reduce the task to creating two-digit numbers. An able child will work comfortably with larger numbers and could be given four digits to work with. This extension will give scope for 24 combinations (provided all the numerals are different and zero does not feature).

In order to assess systematic working, you might ask the child how he/she knows that all the possible combinations have been found. You should typically expect a child who can order three-digit numbers to be able to say them correctly (eg 654 is 'six hundred and fifty-four').

*Addition grid
page 54*

Using numbers (including fractions and negative numbers) It is important for the children to have seen addition bonds presented in a grid before attempting this task. The range of solutions, using counting numbers only, is finite. However, if calculations involving fractions and/or negative numbers are allowed, there is no limit to the number of possible solutions.

A young or less able child will perhaps find a couple of correct solutions. A child with a deeper sense of number conservation may produce solutions based on her/his previous attempts. Using a sense of sequence and pattern is indicative of a wider awareness of number. For example:

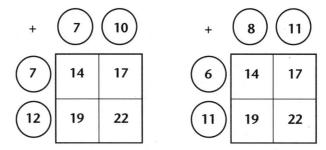

The more able child will confidently work with fractions and/or negative numbers. For example:

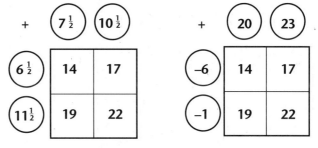

*Missing numbers
page 55*

Solving problems involving addition and subtraction Tens and units blocks could be provided for this task. The problems allow a range of strategies, including trial and improvement and an awareness that addition and subtraction are inverses of one another. In some of the problems, counting on is possible. The solutions are as follows: 4**4** + 3**9** = 83; **3**6 + 34 = 70; 68 + **53** = 121; 74 – **32** = 42; **50** – 18 = 32; 100 – **63** = 37; 362 + **45**9 = 821; 255 + 3**8**5 = 6**4**0; **622 – 266** = 356.

A child who has had relatively little practice in or experience of formal (vertical) computation may encounter some difficulties, particularly with the subtraction problems. Such a child may respond to a units column which apparently show 0 – ? = 7 by placing a 7 in the box. A child with more understanding may try several numbers until a satisfactory solution is found. If regrouping has already been taught, the child may recognise situations in which adding a ten is required to give more units from which to take away. The most able child will adapt strategies to suit each particular problem. The final problem, for example, is particularly difficult, but an able child may find the correct solution through insight and estimation before checking it more rigorously.

See notes for 'Taking away' (page 29)

Pick and mix
page 56

Target 10 and
Target 20
pages 57 and 58

Generating a number investigation Both of these tasks require no preparation other than duplication of the sheet. They both offer scope for many combinations, particularly when numbers other than the counting sequence are introduced. Observe the child working in order to establish whether he/she is using a system. This may not be immediately apparent, and you should discuss the child's progress as he/she works.

In 'Target 10', a less able child may find the inclusion of the corner number in each total, problematic in itself. Some children may, for example, assume that the task simply involves finding three numbers with a total of 10. A child with more confidence and/or ability may find several combinations using trial and improvement. An able child may use a system to find several combinations in sequence – for example, reducing the corner number by one each time. After further work, such a child may establish specific rules such as 'If I have 2 as the corner number, the other two need to total 6.' The most able child should be able to generalise for a set of variables where the three numbers are labelled a, b and c (with b in the corner). In this a situation, the rule which governs members of the set is $a + 2b + c = 10$. As an extension, you could ask for solutions involving fractions and/or negative numbers.

In 'Target 20', most children should have a measure of success using trial and improvement, though some will still have difficulty in following the set instructions after you have talked through them. A child with greater confidence and/or ability may find several examples by controlling the variables (for example, by changing only two of the numbers). After further experimentation, the child may comment on her/his findings and may ultimately arrive at a general statement such as 'The numbers in the grid need to add up to 10, because they're all used twice.' The most able child will deduce that for a square labelled a, b, c and d, the rule governing successful combinations is:
$$2a + 2b + 2c + 2d = 20$$
and thus $a + b + c + d = 10$

Target 100 (a)
page 59

Generating triple bonds to make 100 The target total could be amended to make the task simpler or more complex. It is important that you observe the sequence of examples provided by the child, in order to establish whether a systematic approach being used. If appropriate, extend the assessment by introducing fractions and/or negative numbers.

A less able child may have difficulty in counting in tens, and may be reluctant to venture beyond combinations involving multiples of ten. A more confident and/or able child will find many combinations, and may generate new ones in an identifiable sequence. He/she may work by retaining one number and varying the other two. The most able child will explore negative numbers and/or fractions (with or without prompting), and may realise that the range of answers under these conditions is infinite.

Target 100 (b)
page 60

Selecting a range of number operations for a given total (100) The target total could be amended to make the task easier or more difficult. This open task requires the child to demonstrate his/her ability to work with the four number operations. As such, you will need to remind the child to use all four operations (or fewer if they are unfamiliar with or unable to use certain symbols). You should note the accuracy of the calculations and the range of operations used. The most able child might use fractions and/or negative numbers, combining operations with the help of brackets.

Target 100 (c)
page 61

Calculating complementary pairs totalling 100 You will need to provide the child with a calculator. In detailing the demands of this task, it is important not to suggest any particular method for finding solutions. Emphasise the need for working out 'in your head', and allow calculator use only for checking answers.

While the child is working, observe the accuracy of 'first attempts'. The explanation box (bottom right) will provide further evidence for assessment. The child's ability will be demonstrated primarily by the accuracy and level of independence shown. If possible, ask the child how he/she found the missing numbers. An able child may use knowledge of number bonds to 10 to establish the units digit prior to calculating the number of tens required. Some children may find it difficult to put their methods into words and may need additional support in clarifying their ideas.

Triple bonds
page 62

Adding numbers to a maximum of 30 The child will be at an advantage if he/she has had an opportunity to work on similar puzzles such as magic squares (see Figure 1).

2	7	6
9	5	1
4	3	8

Figure 1

The numbers in each row, column or diagonal add up to 15.

Although the expectation is that the child will add these numbers confidently and accurately, you may wish to offer practical resources. Base 10 materials will not necessarily support this challenge, as the nature of the problem involves some exchange of units and tens. The solutions are shown below right.

A younger or less able child may complete one or two of the four challenges without having any insight into the workings of the task. A more able child may find all the solutions and will persevere with trial and improvement techniques. The most able child will try a range of strategies, such as placing the larger numbers, the smaller numbers, the odd numbers or the even numbers at corners.

	13	
1	**30**	7
16	4	10

	1	
16	**21**	13
4	10	7

	16	
1	**27**	7
10	13	4

	1	
16	**24**	10
7	4	13

Age gap
page 63

Solving a word problem in number independently Provided that the child has experience of written problems, there should be no specific preparation for this task since it is a test of independence in problem-solving. You may need to clarify or amend the language of 'combined age' and 'age gap' as presented in the challenge. It is important that all the child's working is shown and not just the solutions.

A younger or less able child will not necessarily recognise that the two pieces of information given in the task are both necessary to find the answer – that is, that there is only one solution which will give both the correct combined age and the correct age gap. Such a child may also lack confidence in the strategy of trial and improvement. A more able child may be able to pursue a symbolic approach, but is more likely to make a sensible initial estimate and then adjust the ages to fit.

A symbolic (algebraic) method is as follows. If the two people's ages are represented as a and b, then $a + b = 53$ and $a - b = 19$. When these two statements are added together, we get $2a = 72$ and therefore $a = 36$. By substituting the value of a into one of the initial two equations, b can be found: $b = 53 - 36 = 17$ or $b = 36 - 19 = 17$.

In my head 1, 2 and 3
pages 64, 92 and 93

Recalling addition, subtraction, multiplication and division facts These three tasks give you the opportunity to assess the child's mental recall of: addition and subtraction bonds; multiplication and division by 2, 3, 4, 5 and 10; and multiplication and division by 6, 7, 8 and 9. You may wish to restrict the sets of bonds or facts further, and return to the sheet at intervals using different sets of facts or bonds. You could then use the sheet with your own list of questions. The lists suggested here include some bonds or facts which are inverses of each other to check this aspect of recall and understanding. You should also decide on a consistent speed and number of times for reading the questions, and the time allowed for the child to work on each question. You might wish to establish a school or year group policy on this to make the assessments comparable. After the child has finished, you should discuss her/his answers. You may be able to notice patterns in the errors which the child can work on. You and the child can work together to record achievements (at the foot of the sheet) and set future targets.

Addition and subtraction (page 64)				
1. 10 + 3	7. 8 + 5	13. 9 + 7	19. 15 + 4	25. 11 + 9
2. 4 + 8	8. 11 + 5	14. 15 – 12	20. 13 – 5	26. 18 – 14
3. 16 – 5	9. 17 – 9	15. 19 – 11	21. 20 – 8	27. 10 + 7
4. 8 + 9	10. 14 – 8	16. 5 + 11	22. 3 + 15	28. 8 + 4
5. 18 – 8	11. 6 + 7	17. 8 + 6	23. 16 – 7	29. 18 – 9
6. 15 + 2	12. 13 + 6	18. 17 – 2	24. 9 + 9	30. 20 – 5

Multiplication and division (page 92)				
1. 2 × 3	7. 15 ÷ 5	13. 10 × 7	19. 16 ÷ 2	25. 9 × 3
2. 5 × 10	8. 16 ÷ 2	14. 6 × 4	20. 90 ÷ 10	26. 35 ÷ 5
3. 10 × 8	9. 50 ÷ 10	15. 3 × 7	21. 7 × 3	27. 50 ÷ 5
4. 4 × 5	10. 90 ÷ 10	16. 40 ÷ 4	22. 4 × 10	28. 20 ÷ 5
5. 8 × 2	11. 4 × 4	17. 24 ÷ 3	23. 5 × 7	29. 32 ÷ 4
6. 20 ÷ 2	12. 2 × 5	18. 20 ÷ 4	24. 4 × 8	30. 50 ÷ 10

Multiplication and division (page 93)				
1. 8 × 6	7. 24 ÷ 8	13. 8 × 5	19. 81 ÷ 9	25. 8 × 9
2. 10 × 7	8. 90 ÷ 9	14. 10 × 8	20. 80 ÷ 8	26. 18 ÷ 9
3. 9 × 4	9. 48 ÷ 8	15. 8 × 8	21. 6 × 9	27. 54 ÷ 6
4. 6 × 6	10. 36 ÷ 6	16. 40 ÷ 8	22. 8 × 7	28. 49 ÷ 7
5. 6 × 7	11. 9 × 9	17. 45 ÷ 9	23. 10 × 6	29. 42 ÷ 6
6. 18 ÷ 6	12. 7 × 9	18. 56 ÷ 8	24. 7 × 7	30. 36 ÷ 9

Explaining how you did it 1 and 2
pages 65 and 87

Using mental strategies These two sheets are designed to test mental strategies for addition and subtraction (page 65) and multiplication and division (page 87). After each group of four calculations, the child should write down or say how he/she went about doing the calculations. The groups are designed to promote particular strategies or the use of known number facts, but the child may offer different (equally valid) methods. The intended strategies are as follows:

Page 65
• Group 1 – rounding up or down. For 33 + 19, round up the 19 to 20 to get 53, then take away the extra 1 to make 52.
• Group 2 – rounding up the number to make it easier to take away. For 70 – 39, round up the 39 to 40, leaving 30, then add the extra 1 to make 31.
• Group 3 – using doubles to help add. For 15 + 17, use 15 + 15 = 30, then 2 more makes 32.
• Group 4 – using halves. For 80 – 39, change to 80 – 40, then add the extra 1 to make 41.

Page 87
• Group 1 – using the knowledge that × 2 is doubling.
• Group 2 – using the knowledge that ÷ 2 is halving.
• Group 3 – rounding up to more straightforward numbers. For 4 × 99, change to 4 × 100, then take away the 4 to make 396.
• Group 4 – using known number facts to work from.

These tasks may give you the opportunity to assess whether the child is using sensible strategies to work mentally, or whether each calculation he/she approaches is worked on without being connected to other number knowledge. They should also give you the opportunity to assess the child's ability to use mathematical language in explaining her/his own work.

Pick and mix and
Taking away
pages 56 and 66

Addition to 100/Subtraction within 100 These two tasks give you the opportunity to assess the child's ability to add and subtract with numbers to 100. Observe and discuss the child's methods of working with numbers and her/his perception of how calculations should be presented (horizontally, vertically or with just the answer as the result of a mental calculation). The child may be able to work with some numbers but find others more difficult. Some children may use inefficient methods such as counting on or back in ones. This assessment may be of diagnostic value in planning the next phase of work. More confident children may work using only mental methods, and the discussion or written comments will be important for future reference. The layout, presentation and speed of the child's work may also be worth considering.

What's the difference?
1 to 5
pages 67, 68, 69, 70
and 71

Calculating differences within 100 or 1000 using complementary addition and decomposition methods These five tasks are essentially skills-based and require no preparation other than duplication of the sheets. Some children will need access to Base 10 materials. All of the tasks begin with a teacher introduction, talking through an example. Sheets 1 and 2 feature the strategy of complementary addition, applied to two-digit and three-digit numbers respectively. Sheet 3 introduces a further method, and is thus best used after the previous two. Sheets 4 and 5 explore regrouping as a technique with two-digit and three-digit numbers respectively.

Sheets 1 and 4 are appropriate for lower junior children, sheets 2, 3 and 5 for upper junior children. Activities 1 and 2 involve counting on in tens and ones; the latter task also involves counting on in hundreds. Where an error occurs, you should ask the child to talk through her/his solution in order to encourage self-correction. A less able child may need adult support and/or practical number equipment. If the child is comfortable with these two sheets, sheet 3 may offer extension. You should note, however, that the method introduced in the second column may be problematic for all but the most able child. Activities 4 and 5 assess regrouping techniques; where apparatus is needed, Base 10 materials may well be useful.

Countdown to zero
page 72

Understanding place value to 5 figures This task will allow you to assess the child's understanding of place value to tens of thousands. The child's skill in using a calculator appropriately can also be assessed. In order to move down the sequence, the child needs to identify the place value of the digit which changes. For example, to go from 7612 to 7012, the child should enter – 600.

A child who has a sound understanding of place value should be able to work out each step and enter it correctly without experimenting. If you notice the child working by trial and improvement, you may wish to offer

problems involving three-digit numbers in order to check her/his understanding before returning to problems involving thousands and tens of thousands.

Keep on adding and *Keep on taking away* *pages 73 and 85*

Linking repeated addition to multiplication, and repeated subtraction to division These tasks should give you the opportunity to assess whether the child can link repeated addition to multiplication, and link repeated subtraction to division. The child should demonstrate that he/she can record in both ways, for example writing both $9 + 9 + 9 + 9 + 9$ and $5 \times 9 = 45$. He/she should be able to write the missing equivalent operation – for example, given 5×8 the child should write $8 + 8 + 8 + 8 + 8$ alongside.

A child who is secure with multiplication and division facts should be able to complete these sheets by working mentally. A child who works inaccurately or has to work out the answers using apparatus may still understand the link between the two operations; you should question such a child to find out more about her/his understanding, perhaps using numbers from the 2 and 10 times tables only.

Find the product *1 and 2* *pages 74 and 75*

Multiplying two-digit numbers To attempt these tasks, the child will need to have encountered multiplication beyond 10×10, although he/she does not need to have conducted such work using the method provided here. You may prefer to try the child on 'Find the product 1' before presenting the second activity. Once the example has been discussed, the child is required to take over responsibility for setting and solving problems. This will allow the teacher to talk to the child and establish her/his level of understanding. The method shown in both sheets is an example of the distributive law. As a consolidation task, the child could be asked to investigate other ways of subdividing the numbers being multiplied – for example:

$$4 \times 24 \Rightarrow$$

×	5	5	5	5	4	
4	20	20	20	20	16	$\Rightarrow 96$

Your assessment of sheet 1 should be based both on the accuracy of the answers given and on the child's ability to multiply multiples of 10 together. An able child may be aware that, for example, $20 \times 30 = 600$. Alternatively, he/she may describe a method more closely linked to $20 \times 30 = 2 \times 10 \times 3 \times 10 = 6 \times 10 \times 10 = 600$. Such a child could work on sheet 2 as an extension. A

child who is less confident may find that the first sheet offers sufficient challenge. For a child who continues to encounter difficulties, further work (as suggested on the previous page) may provide some consolidation of the distributive law.

Testing times! 1 and 2
pages 76 and 77

Recall/calculation of multiplication facts to 10 × 9 This activity is timed and thus requires a stopclock or watch. The sheets offer scope for revisiting, giving a guide to improvement over time. The numbers across the tops of the grids are a specific focus of assessment. You may prefer to amend the numbers down the left side if you are using the sheet repeatedly.

The tasks are assessments of both speed and accuracy. You should use the outcomes, including the child's responses to the final questions, to inform the next teaching steps.

Testing times! 3
page 78

Recall of multiplication facts within 100 You should make sure that all visual cues, such as number grids and multiplication squares, are removed from classroom display. You may elect to limit the sections to numbers up to 50.

This is a more challenging task than the previous two activities on the same theme. Make sure that the child understands the rules of the task (for example, not duplicating × 10 solutions in successive columns).

Answers:
11 – 20: 2 × 6, 4 × 3, 5 × 3, 4 × 4, 7 × 2, 6 × 3, 8 × 2, 9 × 2, 10 × 2, 5 × 4
21 – 30: 3 × 7, 3 × 8, 3 × 9, 3 × 10, 4 × 6, 4 × 7, 5 × 5, 5 × 6
31 – 40: 4 × 8, 4 × 9, 4 × 10, 5 × 7, 5 × 8, 6 × 6
41 – 50: 5 × 10, 6 × 7, 6 × 8, 9 × 5, 7 × 7
51 – 60: 6 × 10, 9 × 6, 8 × 7
61 – 70: 7 × 10, 8 × 8, 9 × 7
71 – 80: 8 × 10, 9 × 8
81 – 90: 9 × 10, 9 × 9
91 – 100: 10 × 10

A less able child may be unaware of the commutative nature of multiplication (not realising, for instance, that 8 × 2 and 2 × 8 are the same fact), and may struggle to find more than just a few familiar facts. A more able child will have a better recall of table facts, and may begin to generate new ones from her/his knowledge. The most able child will complete the tables quickly and fully, with few omissions and a high level of accuracy.

Number bugs
page 79

Finding factors of numbers Make sure that the child has access to a range of resources, including calculators. Knowledge of the constant facility might be a useful skill to apply in this exercise (if the child is not confident with mental methods). For example, to see whether 4 goes into 24, enter **0 + 4 = = =** etc. (However, some calculators do not operate in this way.)

As well as dealing explicitly with factors, this activity implicitly draws out the child's understanding of multiples and prime numbers. Your assessment should focus on the child's ability to work flexibly with numbers. An able child will use appropriate mathematical vocabulary, and will readily find factors of numbers using mental strategies. For example, with a 40-bug: '2 works (it's even)'; '20 works (because 20 × 2 = 40)'; '10 works (because it's in the 10 times table)'; '5 works (because it's half of 10)'; '8 works (because 5 × 8 is 40)'.

Such a child may also recognise that the factors have complementary partners. Figure 2a shows the pairings of factors. In the case of square numbers, the bugs will be seen to have an odd number of legs (see Figure 2b). Prime-numbered bugs will have only two legs (see Figure 2c).

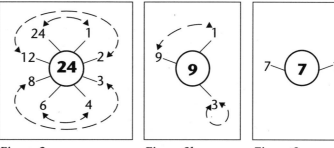

Figure 2a   *Figure 2b*   *Figure 2c*

A child with less experience in number may be over-reliant on calculators and have difficulty with larger numbers. In such a case, it would be helpful to encourage the child to work with numbers below 20.

*Perfect bugs
page 80*

Using knowledge of factors in a practical context Use this task as a follow-up to 'Number bugs'. You may need to demonstrate a couple of 'non-perfect' examples in order to clarify the demands of the task.

The two 'perfect' numbers below 30 are 6 and 28. The next 'perfect' number is a three-digit one, and you are therefore warned not to enter lightly into a search for it!

The task is relatively closed, and thus your judgements of capability will relate to the accuracy and ease with which the child works in number. (The only effective strategy is to try all the numbers systematically.) An able child should be able to investigate numbers below 30 without the aid of a calculator. A less able child will need adult support and intervention throughout the task.

*Puzzling times
page 81*

Solving problems involving multiplication The method of calculation is not specified on the sheet. An able child will establish 'the difference of 1' relationship, and will work comfortably with products up to and beyond 100. An extreme case (for example, comparing 100×100 with 99×101) may be used to test a hypothesis. A child of average or lower ability will work comfortably only within smaller numbers, and may not immediately draw the conclusions expected. Her/his presentation may not be organised, and this will further block the successful identification of patterns and relationships.

The general case can also be considered algebraically: for a number n, multiplying $(n + 1)$ and $(n - 1)$ gives $n^2 + n - n - 1 = n^2 - 1$. This can be demonstrated by graphical means (see Figure 3). These explanations could be discussed with an able child, possibly using squared paper as a resource. It is not anticipated that Key Stage 2 pupils will generate such explanations by themselves, though it is not beyond the scope of able mathematicians who have been introduced to similar ideas on previous occasions.

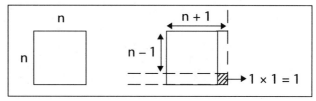

Figure 3

Square numbers 1
page 82

Knowledge and ability to generate square numbers A child who does not immediately recall the square number sequence should be encouraged to calculate them for him/herself, either pictorially (using a squared grid) or numerically. A child with little experience or understanding of square numbers will be unfamiliar with their sequence, and may be unable to generate them without the teacher explaining the rule (1×1, 2×2, 3×3 and so on).

Typically, a child may know some of the square numbers and be familiar with how to generate the unknown ones. A more able child may already know the square numbers to 100. Such a child will readily appreciate the ordinal significance of the thirteenth square number – that is, 13×13. Alternatively, knowing or observing the pattern of differences between successive square numbers might be used to arrive at a correct solution.

Square numbers 2
page 83

Working flexibly with decimals You will need to provide enough calculators to allow the child uninterrupted use of one. It is assumed that the child will have been introduced to the use of the decimal point and will have a basic grounding in decimal fractions. If the calculator has a root function, and the child is familiar with its application, you should discourage her/him from using this as a 'short-cut' technique. If you think the child will be able to work on the task without the prompts, these can be covered prior to photocopying.

This task is much more involved than a child might typically expect when starting the exercise. An able child will work comfortably to several decimal places. It is not a requirement to know the fractional equivalents of numbers to several decimal places, only to recognise when to increase the number and when to reduce it. If the child does not take full account of previous attempts, the task will not be efficiently performed. You will need to examine the sequence of attempts to make a judgement of this.

Cube numbers
page 84

Visualising or calculating cube numbers Provide interlocking cubes (or similar) only if the child is unable to visualise using the pictures on the sheet. While the child is working on the task, you might ask the child how he/she calculates the number of cubes. In some cases, the child may have abstracted the generating rule for any given size of cube (the nth cube will have $n \times n \times n$ or n^3 unit cubes).

A child who is unable to visualise a 3D image from a 2D representation will need cubes to create the shapes. Typically, a child will build up a mental picture based on several 'layers', each layer having the same number of unit cubes. The more able child may abstract a numerical generating rule, and will identify the next cube in the sequence as $6 \times 6 \times 6 = 216$. Such a child may even be able to describe a cube of side n as having a volume $n \times n \times n$.

Keep on taking away
page 85

See notes for page 73.

Mix and match
page 86

Using division flexibly You may opt to present the strip of numbers as pre-cut tiles, and to obscure the lower half of the activity sheet initially. Once the child has completed the upper section, the second part of the task can be explored.

Although the task is essentially one of division, you should not discourage the child from using multiplication to support the search for correct solutions. A younger or less able child will need to use practical resources, such as cubes, to support the completion of this task. Furthermore, the link between multiplication and division facts may not be readily recognised. Although trial and improvement is likely to remain the principal approach to this task, the able child will solve the problems with relative ease. Such a child will recall division facts without recourse to practical materials.

Explaining how you did it 2
page 87

See notes for page 65.

Division One and
Premier Division
pages 88 and 89

Dividing two-digit and three-digit numbers by a single-digit number Although you may opt to provide practical materials for these tasks, it should be recognised that such materials can be cumbersome when working with larger numbers. To divide 87 by 5, for example, involves exchanging 3 tens for 30 units, which gives considerable scope for errors of miscounting.

The examples may need talking through from scratch, starting with the problem alone. The method shown as the first and second examples on both activity sheets is essentially the same, the only difference being that the number has been sub-divided into different-sized 'chunks'. As a consolidation task, ask the child to investigate several different ways of sub-dividing the same problem.

Both sheets allow the child to answer the questions using any method with which he/she is familiar. A child who has considerable experience with division will be comfortable with any one of the methods illustrated. If the concept of division is fully understood, the relationships between the various methods will be recognised. A child with less confidence may restrict her/himself to one preferred method (not necessarily one on the sheet, if it is made clear that a free choice of method is allowed), and may have difficulty recalling some of the number facts demanded by the problems. A child who is unable to complete either sheet may need to explore division exercises more fully, using smaller numbers.

Find four facts
page 90

Using knowledge of number facts and relationships You may prefer to fold this sheet vertically and explore one column, then return to the other at a later date or in a different session.

The child should be able to find all the possible combinations. Thus, in the first two examples:

| **22, 16, 6** | $16 + 6 = 22$ | $6 + 16 = 22$ | $22 - 6 = 16$ | $22 - 16 = 6$ |
| **40, 5, 8** | $5 \times 8 = 40$ | $8 \times 5 = 40$ | $40 \div 5 = 8$ | $40 \div 8 = 5$ |

A child who is not confident with these number relationships will find it difficult to work mentally. He/she may become confused about which number to subtract from after completing the addition partners.

It will be useful to observe the child working in order to gain an insight into the methods he/she is using and the speed at which he/she works. You might ask a very confident child to invent and work through some more examples on the back of the sheet. Being able to devise groups of three numbers demonstrates a strong understanding of the principle behind the pairing of operations.

Fill in the gaps
page 91

Applying the four operations mentally Prepare the instructions you are going to use for each group of children. These will be a sequence of simple operations. You may prefer to work only with addition and subtraction, then go on to multiplication and division at a later time. You may prefer to mix all four operations when assessing more confident or older children. Your decision should be based on what you feel is appropriate for the group of children you are assessing. Also, before beginning, think carefully about the mathematical language you are going to use. You may wish to concentrate on how the operations are applied, and thus use the same terminology throughout. You may prefer to use various terms for the same operations to check the child's understanding of them (see Figure 4).

Possible terminology			
Addition	**Subtraction**	**Multiplication**	**Division**
add	take away	times	share
plus	minus	multiply	divide
... more	... less	multiplied by	divided by
	subtract	double	half

Figure 4

You may wish to set this task in a context by saying 'You have 10 marbles, you give 4 to your friend, you buy 15 more marbles, you share these between you and 2 other friends...' Alternatively, you may prefer to use number operations with no context: 'Start with 10. Add 3. Write your answer. Now add 4. Write your final answer.' Your sets of instructions could be differentiated for various groups of children, and the task could be revisited at different points during the key stage to monitor children's progress.

In my head 2 and *In my head 3* pages 92 and 93

See notes for page 64.

Blank cheques 1 and 2 pages 94 and 95

Reading and writing numbers to 1000 as words These two tasks give you the opportunity to assess the child's ability to read numerals up to and beyond 1000 and write them in words, and to read similar amounts in words and write them as numerals. The task is set in the context of money, and therefore includes the decimal point. It is useful experience for the child to have encountered filling in a cheque. If you do not wish spelling to be a factor in this assessment, you may wish to provide a word list for consultation.

A child with a firm understanding of place value and the ability to spell number names should complete this task quickly and independently. The last two questions on each sheet use amounts beyond £1000; some children may falter here and reveal the need for further work before they can move confidently beyond £1000. The use of the decimal point may also reveal problems to be addressed where children have less experience of money work.

European survey page 96

Converting from one currency to another It will be useful to talk about currencies in other countries and the way that rates of exchange can fluctuate. Some children who have experienced foreign holidays may have a distinct advantage in appreciating the idea of conversion. You may wish to modify the exchange rate table on the sheet to bring the values up-to-date.

The teddy bear prices in sterling (to the nearest pence) are: Spain £13.33; France £15.79; Germany £11.64. Thus France and Germany are the most expensive and the cheapest respectively.

An able child will use the calculator effectively, identifying the sequence of key entries and selecting the appropriate mathematical operations. He/she may also round up/down to the nearest pence. A less able child, or one with little or no experience of conversion, may need support in identifying the appropriate operations. He/she may benefit from a simplified version of the task in which the conversions are easier (for example, £1 = 10 francs).

Below zero page 97

Reading a scale including negative numbers The child should demonstrate the ability to read from a scale and to calculate by moving up and down the scale (including negative numbers) during this task. This work could build on the introduction of negative whole numbers in Year 2 (P3).

Some children may rely on the picture of the thermometer and calculate the answers by counting up and down; others who are more confident in their use and understanding of the scale may internalise the scale and thus operate with little or no direct reference to it. You might suggest to such a child that he/she folds the sheet to conceal the scale. If this happens, you should record it on the sheet.

Real numbers
page 98

Estimating and calculating numbers in real-life contexts This assessment requires the child to think about real numbers in immediate and wider contexts. The child should have the opportunity to use a variety of sources such as atlases, encyclopaedias and other information books. The child will also need to calculate from lists, ask questions and extrapolate from known facts to find out further information. You may prefer to use the final two rows to add questions linked to current cross-curricular work.

A younger child's response may reveal wide gaps between estimates and facts throughout, or as the statistics become further removed from her/his immediate experience of the school and the local area. An older child, or one with greater general knowledge, may make more plausible estimates that are rooted in a more highly-developed sense of number size.

Fractions 1, 2 and 3
pages 99, 100 and 101

Identifying fractions of a whole, ordering fractions on a number line, creating and ordering fractions up to and beyond 1 Sheets 1 to 3 are presented in order of increasing complexity. These tasks are self-contained with the exception of the third, which requires scissors.

These tasks cover a range of elements which are important for a sound understanding of fractions:
• Fractional pieces which are equivalent in value do not necessarily have to be congruent (see the middle section of sheet 1).
• Some fractions can be simplified: 4/6 = 2/3.
• Fractions can have a value greater than 1: 5/3 = 1 2/3.
• The size of a fraction is not determined by the magnitude of the numerator or that of the denominator, but by the **ratio** between them.
The child's responses to each of the three sheets will give important information about her/his understanding of these elements.

Fractions 4
page 102

Calculating fractions of quantities Discouraging the use of calculators for this task focuses the assessment on mental and/or written strategies. The answers are: 1/5 of 20 = 4; 5/6 of 90 = 75; 40p is **4/10** or **2/5** of £1; 138p is **138/100** or **69/50** of £1; 763ml is **763/100** of 1 litre; 20 hours is **20/24** or **10/12** or **5/6** of one day.

The most able child may display several indicators of high achievement: calculating fractions accurately; recognising fractions greater than 1; reducing fractions to their simplest form; and using prior knowledge of common units of measure. Such a child could be extended by asking her/him to convert all of the fractions in these answers to decimals.

Percentages
page 103

Using percentages of a unit whole or a quantity Not allowing the use of calculators for this task focuses the assessment on mental and/or written strategies. The solutions to the second and third problems are:
2. The £66 offer is the best, the others coming to £70 and £68.
3. There are 18 boys in the class.

The initial question involves finding percentages in relation to fractions of a unit whole. The three questions which follow assess the ability to calculate percentages of a quantity. The most able child will work independently, and will show and/or explain all her/his working. A child who is only beginning to appreciate the application of fractions may need support with the second, third and fourth questions.

Spot the pattern
page 104

Recognising and completing number patterns In this assessment, the child is given just enough information to work out each pattern. The range of numbers and the steps can be worked out mentally using knowledge of addition, subtraction and/or multiplication facts. The patterns include sequences from the 9× and 11× tables, even numbers and adding on in 50s and 20s. They do not become more difficult further down the page; but the speed at which the child completes the sequences might be a factor in this assessment.

A child who is working on pattern mentally with confidence should be able to spot and complete the sequences quickly and accurately without any equipment. To extend an able child, you might provide

(doubling) — 4, 8, ... 64

(adding 5, starting with negative numbers) — −10, ... 0, 5

Figure 5

some more pattern fragments to be completed on the back of the sheet, involving less obvious steps and giving only two steps to work from. Two examples are shown in Figure 5. You might also challenge the child to devise her/his own pattern puzzle and try it out on a friend.

What did I do?
page 105

Identifying a rule The child should recognise and describe doubling, ×3 and ÷5, using mathematical language. A child who is confident with using operations and number facts may be much quicker in spotting the rule, checking with the examples and describing the operation. Some children might work more slowly, trying out different ideas. If the child does this, it might provide evidence of her/his using and applying skills, especially if he/she is trying hypotheses, checking, dismissing and then trying an alternative until he/she finds the correct solution.

What comes later?
page 106

Continuing sequences and identifying ordinal patterns This task assesses several skills relating to number patterns: the ability to continue number patterns; identification of the sequence in relation to ordinal position; the ability to predict for an extreme case (100th term); and the ability to make mathematical statements in words.

The solutions are as follows: the number is twice the position in the sequence ($2n$); the number is twice the position in the sequence plus one ($2n + 1$); the number is the position in the sequence multiplied by itself (n^2); the number halves each time (2^{7-n}); the number is the sum of the previous two terms.

A child should typically be able to continue at least some of the sequences given. The majority of children should be able to see the link between the ordinal position of a number in the sequence and its value. An able child will see relatively complex relationships, for example: in the third sequence, the nth term will have a value which is $2n + 1$; consequently the hundredth term will be 201.

Spot the rule
page 107

Pattern spotting and generalising a rule A set of number tiles or cards might provide a useful back-up for pupils who lack confidence in working without practical materials. You will need to encourage the child to look for patterns and to explore with larger numbers, perhaps to check a hypothesis.

The total will always be a multiple of 3, since any sequence of consecutive numbers n, n + 1, n + 2 will have the total $3n + 3$, which is divisible by 3. You will need to encourage the child to talk or write about the results, albeit using words rather than symbols, in order to make a realistic judgement of her/his understanding.

A more able child will not only notice that the middle number is always 1/3 of the total, but may be able to explain why. The third and first terms in the sequence are one more and one fewer, and therefore the three terms must 'average out' as the middle value. Typically, a child will note that multiples of 3 result for all calculations, though he/she may be unable to explain why. A younger or less able child may try a few examples, but see little or no significance in the answers. In such cases, you might encourage the child to use consecutive numbers to start each sequence: first 1 + 2 + 3, then 2 + 3 + 4 and so on. If this is done, you will need to indicate on the sheet that support and direction were given.

Double trouble
page 108

Doubling numbers (mentally and on paper) As the first part of the activity relies on mental skills, no resources are needed. Although practical materials may be requested for the second half of the sheet, you should not suggest possible approaches by presenting such materials in advance.

A child who is confident in number will typically work well in doubling mentally. Such a child may demonstrate flexible strategies for calculation (such as knowledge of doubles: 16 + 16 = 15 + 15 + 1 + 1 = 30 + 2). An able child may already know the term 'infinite' and appreciate what it means. Some children will have difficulty working without paper, and will stop early in the sequence or 'lose track' at some stage. The least confident child will struggle even when working on paper, particularly if he/she is unused to dealing with large numbers.

Input, output 1, 2 and 3
pages 109, 110 and 111

Number relationships in the first quadrant Before attempting this task, the child will need to have carried out some elementary work involving co-ordinates and function machines.

40

Sheets 1 to 3 have been arranged in increasing order of complexity, although all of the functions dealt with produce straight-line graphs. Sheet 1 produces a straight-line graph which intersects the output axis at 3. Changing the function to 'Subtract 3' results in a graph of the same gradient, crossing the output axis at –3. Sheet 2 produces an interesting representation of the 'story of 10': all the addition complements of 10. If inputs of value greater than 10 are selected, the outputs would need to be negative. This would necessitate extending the graph beyond the first quadrant.

Sheet 3 demonstrates how multiplying the input up or down affects the gradient of the resulting line. The child should notice that the function 'Treble it' produces a steeper line than 'Double it', and should predict that 'Halve it' will produce a less steep line than either. Stating the numerical values of the gradients should not be expected at this level.

Trampoline party
page 112

Solving a problem involving several stages of calculation The child should be familiar with basic problems involving money before undertaking this task. You may prefer to have the children produce an advertising brochure in order to give the task a sense of reality. You may need to explain the purpose of a one-off booking fee (to cover the costs of administration and staffing).

A child who lacks confidence in this type of work may need to be supported and given appropriate resources (such as a calculator) to calculate with. You should expect a child of average ability to work out the total amount using the correct notation for pounds and pence. Although the strategy for calculation may not necessarily depend on the use of standard (taught) methods, it should nevertheless be well-organised and correct. An able child could be given supplementary questions, such as the calculation of costs per head or the cash required for a deposit of (for example) 15%.

A sound deal
page 113

Solve problems involving finding unknowns Some pupils may benefit from being shown actual examples of the articles shown on the activity sheet, in order to make the context more 'real'. It is important to stress that the second statement price of each item does not vary in this problem (since the child will be familiar with variable prices in real life). By subtracting the second statement from the first, it can be established that the compact disc is priced at £11.50. Substituting this into one of the original statements gives a price of £6.50 for the audio tape.

A less able child will fail to recognise that the two statements are both necessary to find the answer. If the child recognises this, he/she may still try random amounts to see they work in both cases. Although there are various ways of approaching the task, the child will need to apply strategies involving logic to complete this exercise effectively. An able child will work through the task without support or direction, and may check her/his answer by working through both statements with the unknowns filled in.

Shopper's choice
page 114

Adding up money and giving change within £10 You may prefer to make coins available from the beginning of this task. The sheet should be relatively self-explanatory. The principal role of the teacher is to observe the strategies used to resolve this challenge.

The three items purchased were a beach ball, a pack of cards and a cassette. The total price is £8.88. The change from £10 is £1.12. The range of possible costs (extension task) is from £10.64 (CD, cards, beach ball) to £8.88 (beach ball, cards, cassette).

An able child will work through this task with ease, making an accurate judgement of what three items to select by approximating the total cost of randomly selected items. The extension suggested above will give such a child an opportunity to explore further. A child with less confidence may lack strategies for working through this task, and may not readily make use of counting on to calculate the change ('shopkeeper's addition'). The least able child will need support with both the language and the associated mathematical content.

Find it!
page 115

Solving a problem using a calculator Make sure that each child has access to a calculator. It is assumed that the child will be familiar with the basic functions of the calculator.

At first, this task appears to be highly complex through its sheer open-endedness. For some, finding an efficient route through the task may be too difficult. In such cases, the challenge can be modified to finding a solution which is close to 8023. Alternatively, some of the digits in the solution could be written in the spaces before the sheet is copied (see right). The more digits that are added, the easier the problem becomes.

One particularly effective strategy is to consider how the units digit (3) of the target number might be obtained. Since 3 can only result from the product of 1 and 3, this significantly reduces the number of possibilities. Knowledge of the fact that multiplication and division are inverses will further support the solving of this task. A quick and effective approach is to divide 8023 by different two-digit numbers ending in 1 or 3, thus narrowing down the range of trial and improvement. The solution is 113 × 71.

For a less able child, the challenge of finding numbers which give a product of the order of 8023 (that is, about 8000) will be sufficiently demanding. The majority of children are likely to have a reasonable sense of the scale of possible solutions but may not apply logic to consider how the units digit of the product can be achieved. An able child will try two-digit numbers ending in 3 or 1, and may even attempt to divide these into the target number to give the three-digit solution. Such a child will recognise that both numbers must be counting (whole) numbers.

Round the block
page 116

Explaining patterns and relationships (in words/symbols) You may need to make paper (squared or plain) available. The sheet is arranged as a progression of tasks. In the broadest terms, the assessment of this activity should be based on the extent of the child's progress through the three sections.

The first section deals with generating further rectangles which all have the same perimeter. From this task, or through scrutiny of the completed table, the child should realise that the perimeter is always double the sum of the length and the width. The child's attempt to describe this will need to be assessed for its accuracy and the use of precise mathematical vocabulary. The final part of the sheet requires the child to generalise for any rectangle having dimensions a and b. The following solutions (and any others which are mathematically equivalent) are acceptable: perimeter = a + b + a + b; perimeter = 2a + 2b; perimeter = 2 (a + b). The use of symbols may be difficult for some children to appreciate.

Nearest numbers
page 117

Using number skills to solve problems Although you may opt to provide calculators, excluding their use on this occasion may provide additional assessment evidence (of fluency in mental calculation).

Part of the complexity of this task relates to the use of specific mathematical vocabulary. You should therefore support the child with reading as necessary, but not in a way that suggests what operations or numbers to use. If it becomes necessary, for example, to explain what a set of consecutive numbers is, this will invalidate part of the assessment focus, but will still allow scope for mathematical investigation.

The answers are: 13, 14, 15, 16 and 17; 9 and 11 or 33 and 3; 14 and 28; 7, 8 and 9. An able child will recognise the mathematical language and apply this knowledge in solving the problem. He/she may use algebra and/or a calculator to derive a 'theoretical' solution to which the actual solution is an approximation. Most children will probably need some support with the interpretation of the questions, but will have some success in finding solutions. A child with less experience in work of this type may lack perseverance, and may also lack an organised strategy (such as trial and improvement or algebra) in searching for solutions.

Hundreds and
thousands
page 118

Powers of 10 and place value A calculator will be useful for most of this task and is explicitly required for the final question. The solutions are: ten or 10; 1000, one thousand; 6800p, £68.00; 1.8, £1.80.

The first question is relatively straightforward, and leads the child into the problem that follows. The second and third tasks can be used to assess a range of skills: the ability to write large numbers in numerals and words; the ability to multiply by 10 and by 100; and the ability to judge the 'reasonableness' of an answer. The final question involves finding a calculator output which, in most displays, will require interpretation. Unless the calculator has a 'fix' facility which allows the answer to be given to two decimal places, the solution found for 9.00 ÷ 5 will be 1.8. This task therefore assesses both the child's ability to select appropriate mathematics to find the correct solution and the child's ability to interpret 1.8 as £1.80 in this context.

A child who has difficulty with several of these questions may lack experience in working with large numbers and investigating what happens under multiplication by 10, 100 and 1000. Although the majority of children may be surprised by the calculator output in the final question, they should be able to interpret (or have strategies to make sense of) the answer obtained.

Name   *Date*

Number chains

Demonstrates that the child can write order numbers to 1000.

Using and applying
- *Records accurately.*
- *Checks own work.*

Prepare suitable chains of numbers (see Teachers' notes). Ask the child to write the start or the end number in each chain as you say it. Ask the child to fill in all the missing numbers from start to end or from end to start. Check the child's answers with him/her.

Note whether the child can:
❏ write three-digit numbers accurately
❏ count and write numbers in sequence going forwards
❏ count and write numbers in sequence going backwards in the range
_____ to _____

Teacher comments

start

end

start

end

start

end

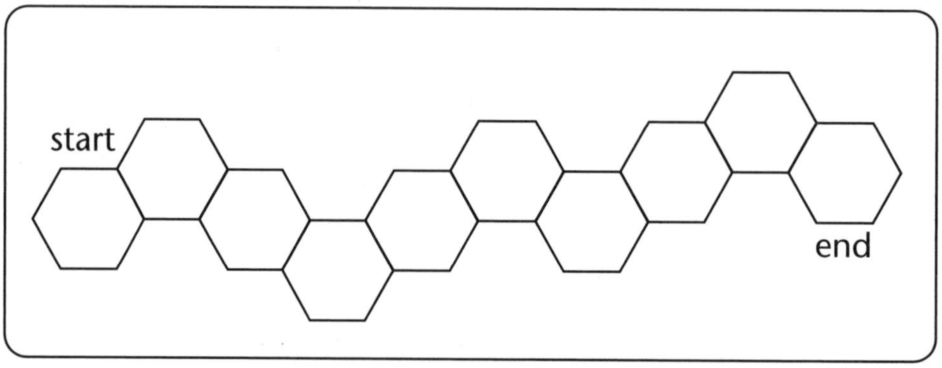

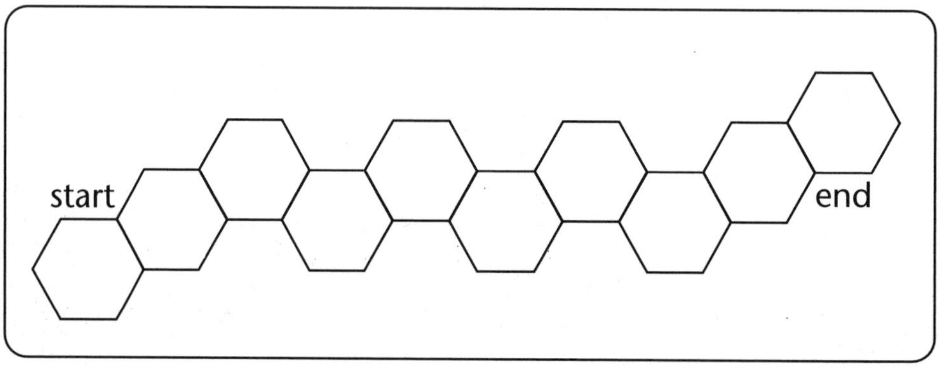

start

end

start

end

Teachers' notes, page 22

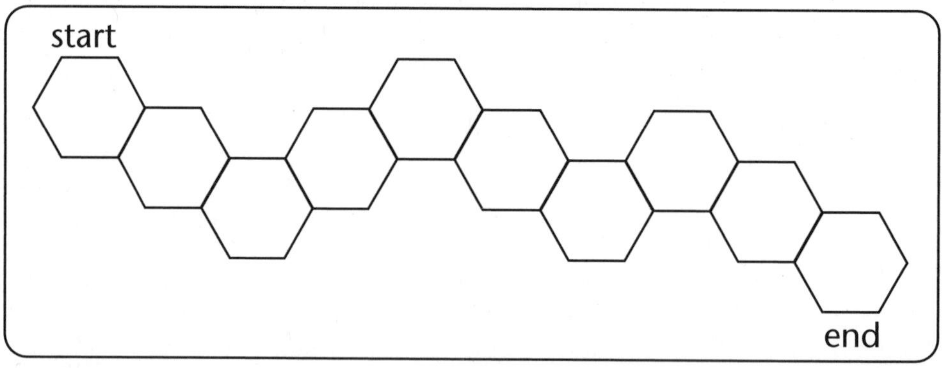

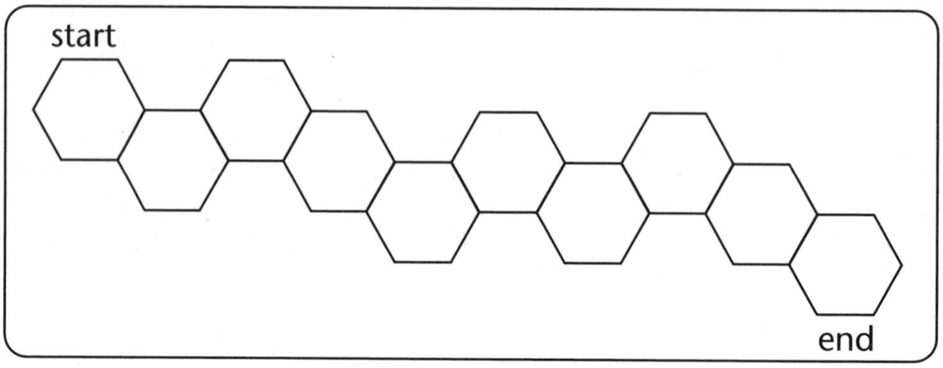

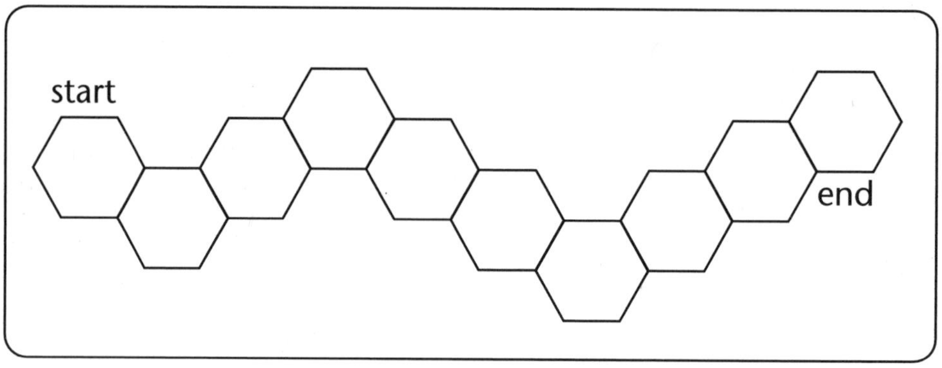

Name

Date

The morning post

Demonstrates that the child can order three-digit numbers.

Using and applying
- *Checks results.*
- *Develops own strategy.*
- *Identifies necessary information for task.*

Give each child a set of five prepared envelopes (see Teachers' notes). Ask the child to order these so they can be delivered efficiently, recording the arrangement on the sheet, then mix up the set again and pass it on. When each child has sorted all of the sets, give the child an extra envelope and ask her/him to fit it into the last group in the correct place.

Note whether the child can:
❏ order 3-digit numbers
❏ fit numbers in between in the range _____ to _____.

Teacher comments

Teachers' notes, page 22

Quick off the grid 1

Complete each of the following grids:

Demonstrates the child's ability to count on or back within 100.

Demonstrates the child's ability to recognise and complete patterns.

Using and applying
• *Develops own strategies.*
• *Looks for patterns.*
• *Explains reasoning.*

Provide one copy of the sheet per child. Explain that the numbers in each grid are arranged in a particular sequence. The task is to identify the nature of the steps along the rows and down the columns. Talk to the child during (or after) the task to support your assessment (see below).

Note whether the child:
❑ talks about strategies
❑ counts on in steps
❑ counts back in steps
❑ works unaided

Teacher comments

2					12
					24
					48

18				6	
				5	
					1

62	59				47
					50
					59

Teachers' notes, page 22

Quick off the grid 2

Complete each of the following grids:

Demonstrates the child's ability to count on or back within and beyond 100.

Using and applying
• *Develops own strategies.*
• *Looks for patterns.*
• *Explains reasoning.*

Provide one copy of the sheet per child. Explain that the numbers in each grid are arranged in a particular counting sequence. The task is to identify the nature of the steps along the rows and down the columns. Talk to the child during (or after) the task to support your assessment (see below).

Note whether the child :
❑ talks about strategies
❑ counts on in steps
❑ counts back in steps
❑ works unaided

Teacher comments

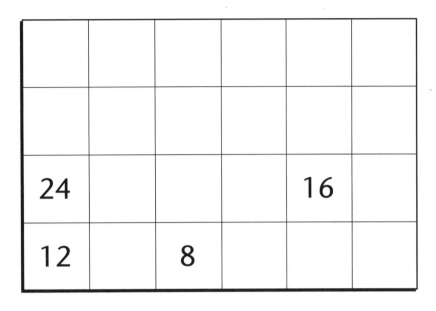

24				16	
12		8			

					25
2				6	

66	71				
96					121

Teachers' notes, page 22

Name *Date*

Which is closer? 1

Join to show.

Demonstrates that the child can find differences between numbers to 100. Demonstrates that the child can round numbers to the nearest 10.

Using and applying
• *Works mentally.*
• *Understands and uses mathematical language.*

Ask the child to join each middle number to the number on either side that it is closest to. You may wish to ask the child how he/she arrived at particular answers.

Note whether the child can:
❏ round numbers up or down to the nearest 10

Teacher comments

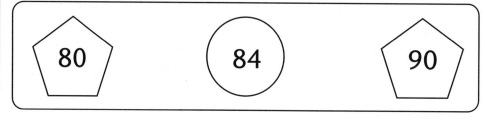

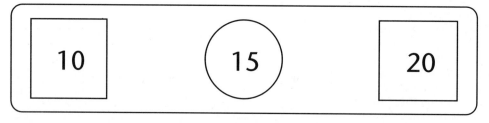

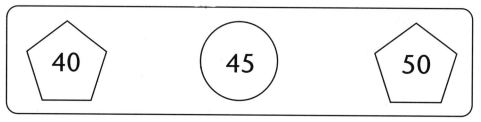

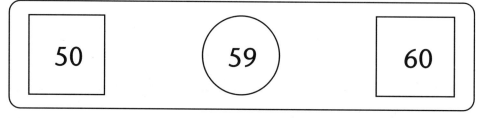

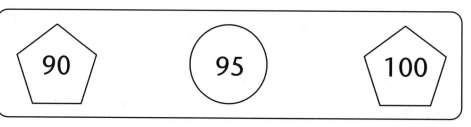

Teachers' notes, page 23

Name

Date

Which is closer? 2

Join to show.

Demonstrates that the child can use mental methods to find differences between numbers to 1000. Demonstrates that the child can round three-digit numbers to the nearest 100.

Using and applying
- *Works mentally.*
- *Understands and uses mathematical language.*

Ask the child to join each middle number to the number on either side that it is closest to. Ask the child to record how much closer one number is than another in each case (optional).

Note whether the child can:
❑ round tens numbers up or down to the nearest 100

Teacher comments

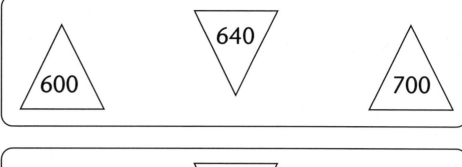

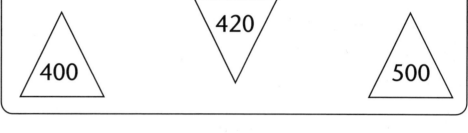

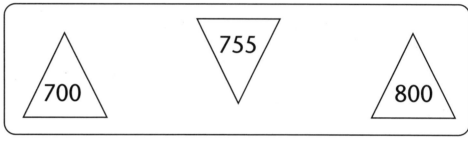

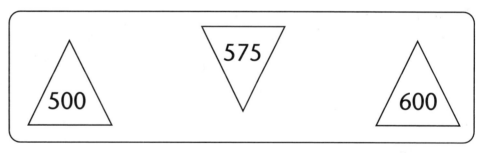

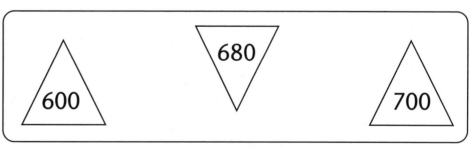

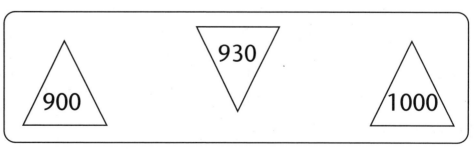

Teachers' notes, page 23

Name   *Date*

Jumping in tens

How many jumps of 10 to get from start to finish?

Start at   Finish at

Demonstrates that the child can count on or back in 10s from a variety of points. Demonstrates that the children record three-digit numbers accurately.

Using and applying
• *Uses own choice of method.*
• *Explains own method.*
• *Uses awareness of pattern.*

Before copying the sheet, fill in the three start and finish numbers (see Teachers' notes). Ask the child to work out how many jumps of 10 are needed to get from the start to the finish in each case. Allow the child a free choice of equipment. Ask the child to write or dictate an explanation of her/his method. Finally, ask the child to write out a complete sequence using the chain of spaces at the foot of the page.

Note whether the child can:
❑ jump accurately in 10s
❑ explain own methods
❑ choose equipment sensibly
❑ record three-digit numbers accurately

Teacher comments

 _____ jumps

 _____ jumps

 _____ jumps

Describe how you worked out the answers:

Teachers' notes, page 23

Name

Date

Adding fives

Demonstrates that the child can recognise and describe a pattern. Demonstrates that the child can make sensible predictions based on investigation.

Using and applying
• *Checks results and considers whether they are reasonable.*
• *Looks for pattern in results.*

Ask the child to work through the three examples, then use this experience to predict what will happen at other starting points. Ask the child to justify her/his predictions to you. The child could test her/his predictions on the back of the sheet.

Note whether the child can:
❏ apply the pattern
❏ make and justify a prediction
❏ check results

Teacher comments

start at 0 +5		start at 1 +5		start at 3 +5	
t	u	t	u	t	u
	5		6		3
1	0	1	1		8

What pattern can you see in the units column?

_____

_____

_____

What will happen if you start at 2?

_____

_____

_____

_____

_____

_____

_____

_____

_____

What will happen if you start at 4?

_____

_____

_____

_____

_____

_____

_____

_____

_____

Teachers' notes, page 24

Spot the pattern

Demonstrates that the child can spot a recurring pattern.

Using and applying
• *Identifies and obtains information on which to base conclusions.*
• *Checks results.*
• *Looks for segments of pattern.*

Ask the child to investigate a times table to find the recurring pattern in the units column. Ask the child to check that this pattern does recur. Ask the child to write down what else he/she has noticed about the pattern; through discussion, encourage the child to explain the pattern and find connections between related patterns (such as the 2× and 4× tables).

Note whether the child can:
❑ identify the recurring sequence
❑ check her/his results

Teacher comments

In the 5 times table, the units numbers make the pattern 0 5 0 5 0 5. Choose another times table and see if you can spot a pattern in the units numbers.

I chose the _____ times table.

The units pattern I found was:

What else I noticed:

Name

Date

All in order

Demonstrates the child's understanding of place value.

Using and applying
• *Selects and uses appropriate mathematics.*
• *Organises and checks work.*

Prepare the sheet by writing three numerals on the digit cards at the bottom. Tell the child to cut out the digit cards and then manipulate them to create different three-digit numbers. The child should record these numbers and then order them. Talk to the child to support your assessment (see below).

Note whether the child:
❑ works systematically
❑ reads the numbers aloud correctly (place value)
❑ orders the numbers correctly
❑ works without support

Teacher comments

I can make three-digit numbers with these digit cards.

Teachers' notes, page 24

Here are the numbers in order:

☐ , ☐ , ☐ ,

☐ , ☐ , ☐

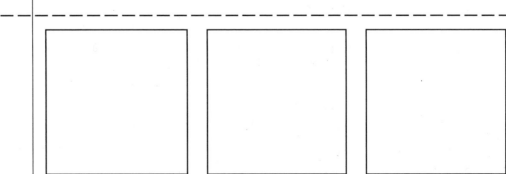

Name   *Date*

Addition grid

Demonstrates the child's ability to use numbers flexibly (including fractions and negative numbers, if appropriate).

Using and applying
• *Sees patterns in answers.*
• *Recognises the infinite nature of the (extended) task.*
• *Applies knowledge of pattern to create further solutions.*
• *Extends the task.*

You will need to discuss and observe the child's work to identify whether new solutions are random or are generated from an awareness of sequence. If appropriate, encourage the child to explore the extension task on the back of the sheet or on further paper.

Note whether the child:
❑ recognises pattern
❑ generates new arrangements from earlier ones
❑ uses fractions
❑ uses negative numbers

Teacher comments

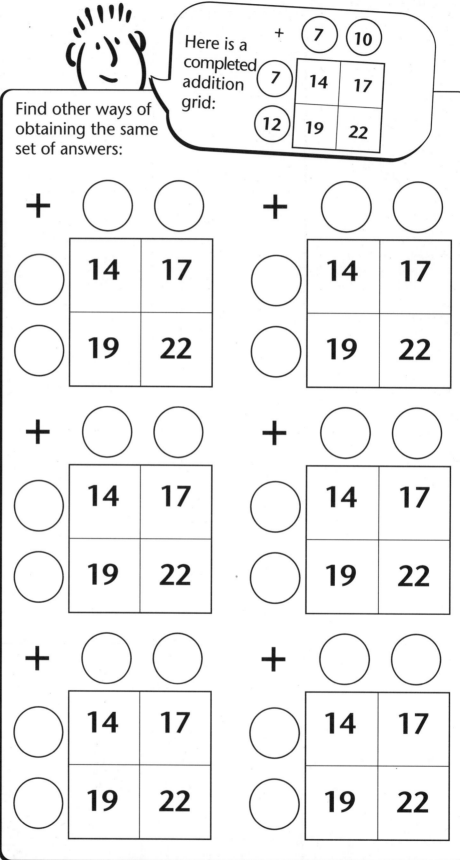

Here is a completed addition grid:

Find other ways of obtaining the same set of answers:

Would it be possible to find solutions using fractions? How about negative numbers?

Teachers' notes, page 25

Name

Date

Missing numbers

Demonstrates the child's ability to solve problems involving addition and subtraction.

Using and applying
• Selects mathematics required.
• Considers reasonableness of answers.
• Finds ways to overcome difficulties.
• Tries different approaches.

Provide practical materials if necessary, but discourage the use of calculators on this occasion. Talk to the child to identify whether he/she appreciates the idea of inverse functions and discuss the strategies he/she has used.

Note whether the child:
❑ uses inverse functions to find solutions.

Strategies used:

Teacher comments

$$\begin{array}{r} 4\ \square \\ +\ \square\ 9 \\ \hline 8\ 3 \end{array}$$

$$\begin{array}{r} \square\ 6 \\ +\ 3\ \square \\ \hline 7\ 0 \end{array}$$

$$\begin{array}{r} 6\ 8 \\ +\ \square\ \square \\ \hline 1\ 2\ 1 \end{array}$$

$$\begin{array}{r} 7\ 4 \\ -\ \square\ \square \\ \hline 4\ 2 \end{array}$$

$$\begin{array}{r} 5\ \square \\ -\ \square\ 8 \\ \hline 3\ 2 \end{array}$$

$$\begin{array}{r} 1\ 0\ 0 \\ -\ \square\ \square \\ \hline 3\ 7 \end{array}$$

$$\begin{array}{r} 3\ 6\ \square \\ +\ \square\ \square\ 9 \\ \hline 8\ 2\ 1 \end{array}$$

$$\begin{array}{r} 2\ 5\ 5 \\ +\ \square\ 8\ \square \\ \hline 6\ \square\ 0 \end{array}$$

Use three 6s and three 2s to make this statement correct:

$$\begin{array}{r} \square\ \square\ \square \\ -\ \square\ \square\ \square \\ \hline 3\ 5\ 6 \end{array}$$

Teachers' notes, page 25

Name

Date

Pick and mix

19 36 25 43 51 28

Demonstrates that the child can add two-digit numbers correctly.

Using and applying
• *Uses mental methods or equipment.*
• *Explains own methods.*

Ask the child to use the numbers on the sheet to make ten different addition calculations. When the child has finished, ask her/him to write down or tell you what he/she used. Scribe for the child if necessary.

Note whether the child can:
❑ add two-digit numbers accurately

Method used:

Teacher comments

How did you add the numbers?

Teachers' notes, page 26

Name   *Date*

Target 10

Demonstrates the child's ability to generalise a number investigation.

Using and applying
• *Uses trial and improvement.*
• *Identifies a rule for new combinations.*
• *Explains reasoning.*

Talk through the example on the sheet. Encourage the child to record both successful and unsuccessful attempts in the space provided, continuing on the back of the sheet if necessary. Discuss the question at the foot of the sheet, drawing out the child's awareness of the underlying rule (see Teachers' notes).

Note whether the child:
❏ uses trial and improvement
❏ identifies a generating pattern or rule

Teacher comments

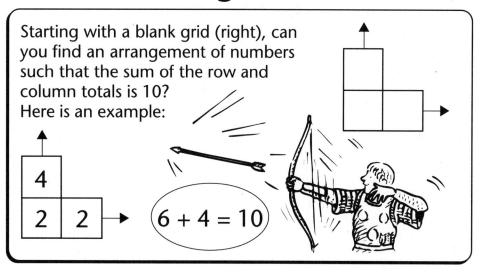

Starting with a blank grid (right), can you find an arrangement of numbers such that the sum of the row and column totals is 10?
Here is an example:

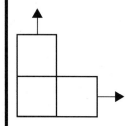

$6 + 4 = 10$

Now find some more combinations of your own:

What did you notice?

Teachers' notes, page 26

Target 20

Demonstrates the child's ability to generalise a number investigation.

Using and applying
* *Uses trial and improvement.*
* *Identifies a rule for new combinations.*
* *Explains reasoning.*

Talk through the example on the sheet. Encourage the child to record both successful and unsuccessful attempts in the space provided, continuing on the back of the sheet if necessary. Discuss the question at the foot of the sheet, drawing out the child's awareness of the underlying rule (see Teachers' notes).

Note whether the child:
❏ uses trial and improvement
❏ identifies a generating pattern or rule

Teacher comments

Starting with a blank grid, can you find a set of four numerals such that the sum of the column and row totals is 20? Here is an example:

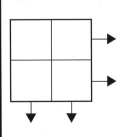

$$7 + 3 + 4 + 6 = 20$$

Now find some more combinations of your own:

What did you notice?

Name   *Date*

Target 100 (a)

Demonstrates the child's ability to generate triple bonds of 100.

Using and applying
• *Uses pattern to generate new combinations.*
• *Checks results.*
• *Uses negative numbers.*

Talk through the example with the child. Encourage the able child to use both positive and negative numbers. Assess the child's level of independence (see below).

Note whether the child:
❏ works without support
❏ works without apparatus
❏ generates new combinations using pattern

Teacher comments

The numbers at the corners add up to the number inside the triangle:

20

100

40   40

Find some triangle arrangements of your own with the same total.
Draw them below.

Teachers' notes, page 26

Target 100 (b)

Find some different ways of making 100 using any number operation (+, −, ×, ÷).

Demonstrates the child's ability to select a range of number operations for a given target total (100).

Using and applying
• *Selects appropriate mathematics.*
• *Looks for pattern in results.*
• *Explains reasoning.*

Talk through the activity and the example given as a solution. Encourage a diversity of responses, including fractions and negative numbers. Observe and discuss the child's work to complete the assessment checklist below.

Note whether the child:
❏ works without support
❏ works without apparatus
uses the operations:
❏ +
❏ −
❏ ×
❏ ÷

Other significant evidence:

Teacher comments

———————

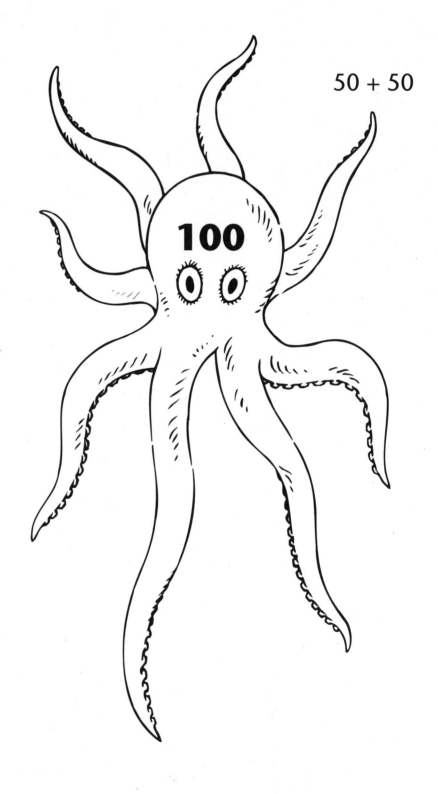

50 + 50

100

How many **different** ways do you think there are?

Name

Date

Target 100 (c)

Demonstrates the child's ability to calculate complementary pairs totalling 100 mentally.

Using and applying
• *Selects appropriate mathematics.*
• *Develops own mathematical strategies.*

Discuss the task, referring to the example provided. Wherever possible, discuss the methods used by the child in order to raise her/his awareness of possible strategies. Make a calculator available for checking.

Note whether the child:
❑ works without support
❑ works without number apparatus
❑ uses calculator appropriately (for checking)

Teacher comments

Work out (in your head) the numbers which need to be added to those given below to make 100. The first one has been done for you.

Check your answers with a calculator and tick your correct solutions.

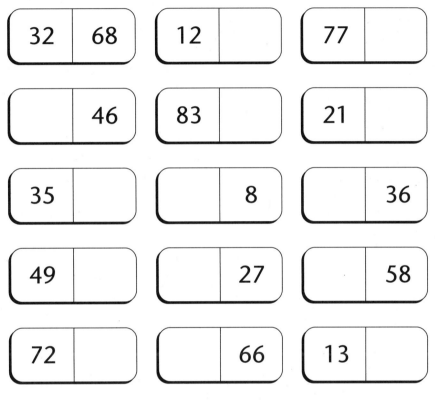

32	68
12	
77	

	46
83	
21	

35	
	8
	36

49	
	27
	58

72	
	66
13	

Explain how you worked out the answers:

Demonstrates the child's ability to add numbers to a maximum of 30.

Demonstrates the child's ability to solve logic problems involving addition.

Using and applying
• *Uses different strategies.*
• *Applies logic.*
• *Recognises patterns.*

Observe how the child works and note her/his solutions. Discuss the child's approaches if they are not immediately obvious. Detail any additional support that is required.

Note whether the child finds solutions by:
❑ trial and improvement
❑ logic

Teacher comments

Triple bonds

Cut out the numbers at the bottom of this sheet. Arrange them on each of the four triangles so that the total along each side of the triangle is equal to the number inside the triangle.

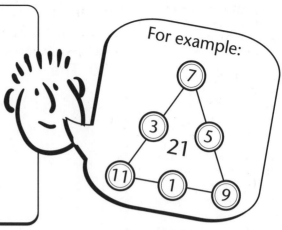

For example:

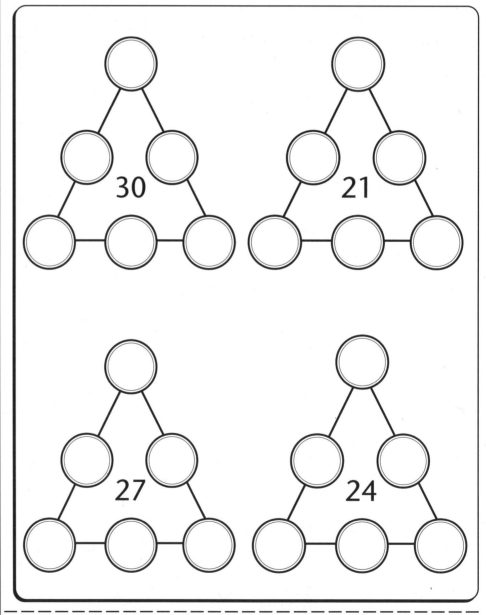

Teachers' notes, page 27

✂ - - - - - - - - - - - - - - - - - - -

(1)   (4)   (7)   (10)   (13)   (16)

SCHOLASTIC PORTFOLIO ASSESSMENT
Maths Key Stage 2

Name   *Date*

Age gap

Two people have a combined age of 53 years. There is an age gap (difference) of 19 years between them. What are the ages of the two people?

Show **all** your working:

Demonstrates the child's ability to solve a word problem in number independently.

Using and applying
• *Finds ways to overcome difficulties.*
• *Uses trial and improvement.*

Read through the task with the child, making sure that the language is not creating difficulty. Use observation and/or discussion to identify the strategies employed by the child.

Note what strategies the child uses:
❑ trial and improvement

Teacher comments

Teachers' notes, page 28

Name   *Date*

In my head 1

Demonstrates that the child can recall and use addition bonds to 20. Demonstrates that the child can recall and use subtraction facts to 20.

Using and applying
• *Works accurately.*

Ask the child 30 addition and subtraction questions orally (see Teachers' notes). The child should work these out mentally and write the answers in the boxes. After the task is completed, go through the answers to check them. Help the child to list (at the foot of the page) the +/– bonds he/she knows and the ones to be worked on.

Note whether the child can recall and use:

+ –
❑ ❑ 11
❑ ❑ 12
❑ ❑ 13
❑ ❑ 14
❑ ❑ 15
❑ ❑ 16
❑ ❑ 17
❑ ❑ 18
❑ ❑ 19
❑ ❑ 20

Teacher comments

1.	2.	3.
4.	5.	6.
7.	8.	9.
10.	11.	12.
13.	14.	15.
16.	17.	18.
19.	20.	21.
22.	23.	24.
25.	26.	27.
28.	29.	30.

I know

I am working on

Teachers' notes, page 28

Name

Date

Explaining how you did it 1

Demonstrates that the child can use flexible strategies to work out addition and subtraction calculations.

Using and applying
• *Develops own strategies.*
• *Looks for ways to overcome difficulties.*
• *Explains methods used.*

Ask the child to complete each group of calculations. When the child completes each group, ask her/him to describe any methods he/she used to work out the calculations. Scribe for the child if necessary.

Note whether the child can recognise and use these strategies:
❑ doubling
❑ halving
❑ rounding up and down
❑ using known number facts

Teacher comments

$33 + 19 =$

$29 + 45 =$

$41 + 27 =$

$59 + 23 =$

_____

_____

_____

_____

_____

_____

_____

_____

$70 - 39 =$

$89 - 43 =$

$62 - 19 =$

$90 - 39 =$

$15 + 17 =$

$25 + 26 =$

$48 + 49 =$

$39 + 43 =$

_____

_____

_____

_____

_____

_____

_____

_____

$80 - 39 =$

$100 - 51 =$

$88 - 42 =$

$68 - 33 =$

Teachers' notes, page 29

Name

Date

Taking away

73

18   64   21   49   70   55   48   12   14   27

Demonstrates that the child can subtract two-digit numbers correctly.

Using and applying
- *Uses mental methods or equipment.*
- *Explains own methods.*

Ask the child to subtract each of the numbers in squares from the number in the hexagon, writing down the answers in the space provided. When the child has finished recording, ask her/him to write down or tell you what methods he/she used. Scribe for the child if necessary.

Note whether the child can:
❑ subtract two-digit numbers correctly

Notes/analysis of method:

Teacher comments

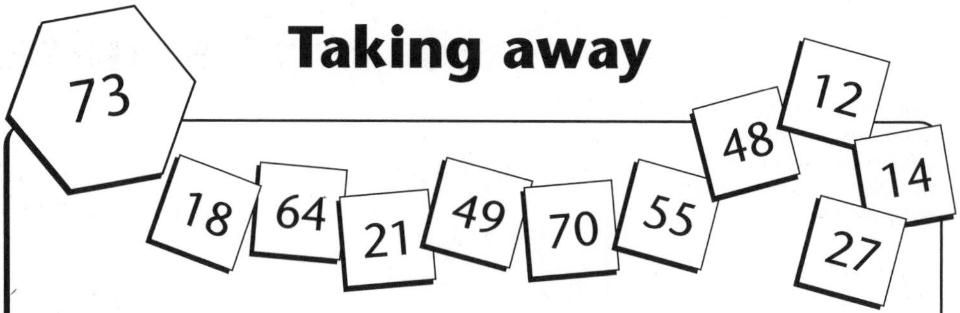

How did you subtract the numbers?

_____

_____

_____

_____

Teachers' notes, page 29

Name

Date

What's the difference? 1

Demonstrates the child's ability to calculate differences using complementary addition (within 100).

Using and applying
• *Tries different mathematical approaches.*
• *Checks results and considers whether they are reasonable.*

Explain the method illustrated in the example if the child is not familiar with it. Provide number lines and/or Base 10 materials if necessary.

Note whether the child:
❑ works without support
❑ works without apparatus
❑ checks and corrects results

Teacher comments

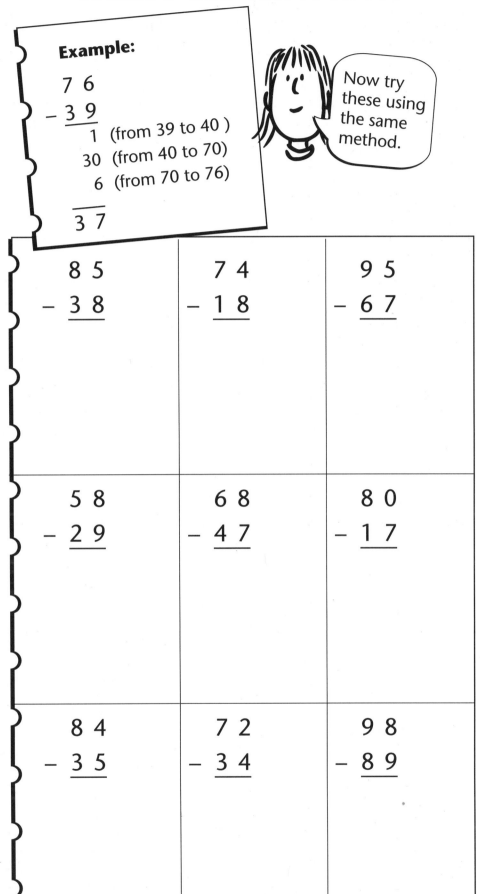

Example:

```
  7 6
-  3 9
       1   (from 39 to 40 )
      30   (from 40 to 70)
       6   (from 70 to 76)
   ------
   3 7
```

Now try these using the same method.

```
  8 5        7 4        9 5
-  3 8      - 1 8      - 6 7


  5 8        6 8        8 0
-  2 9      - 4 7      - 1 7


  8 4        7 2        9 8
-  3 5      - 3 4      - 8 9
```

Teachers' notes, page 30

What's the difference? 2

Demonstrates the child's ability to calculate differences using complementary addition (within 1000).

Using and applying
*   *Tries different mathematical approaches.*
*   *Checks results and considers whether they are reasonable.*

Explain the method illustrated in the example. Provide number lines and/or Base 10 materials if necessary.

Note whether the child:
❑ works without support
❑ works without apparatus
❑ finds correct answers
❑ checks and corrects results

Teacher comments

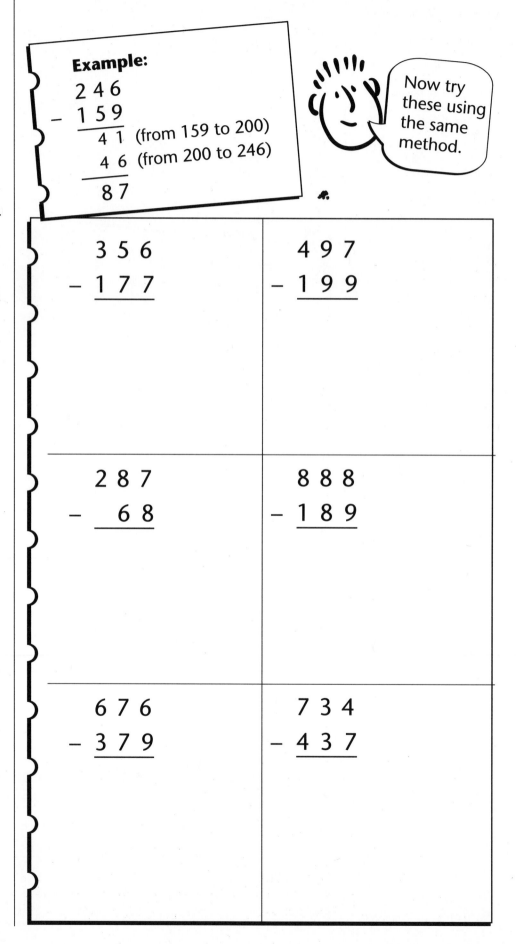

Example:

```
  2 4 6
- 1 5 9
─────────
    4 1   (from 159 to 200)
    4 6   (from 200 to 246)
─────────
    8 7
```

Now try these using the same method.

```
  3 5 6            4 9 7
- 1 7 7          - 1 9 9
```

```
  2 8 7            8 8 8
-   6 8          - 1 8 9
```

```
  6 7 6            7 3 4
- 3 7 9          - 4 3 7
```

Teachers' notes, page 30

Name   *Date*

What's the difference? 3

Demonstrates the child's ability to calculate differences using two different methods.

Using and applying
• *Uses different mathematical methods.*
• *Checks results.*
• *Explains reasoning.*

Discuss the two approaches shown in the examples. Provide additional support and/or materials if necessary. Discuss the child's use of both approaches when the calculations have been completed, and scribe the child's comments in response to the final questions.

Note whether the child:
❑ checks and corrects own work
❑ works without apparatus
❑ works without support

Teacher comments

Here are two different ways to solve the same problem.

Example:

```
  2 3 7
–   8 9
```

```
    1 1   (from 89 to 100)
  1 0 0   (from 100 to 200)
    3 7   (from 200 to 237)
  ─────
  1 4 8
```

Example:

```
  2 3 7
–   8 9
  ─────
  1 3 7   (237 – 100)
    1 1   (100 – 89)
  ─────
  1 4 8
```

Solve these problems using both methods each time.

3 7 2 – 9 8	3 7 2 – 9 8
4 3 8 – 7 7	4 3 8 – 7 7
2 2 2 – 8 4	2 2 2 – 8 4

Which method do you prefer? Why?

What's the difference? 4

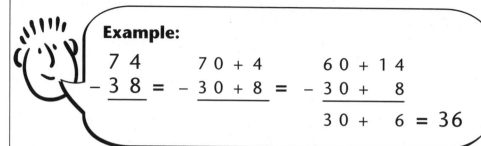

Example:

$$\begin{array}{r} 7\,4 \\ -\ 3\,8 \end{array} = \begin{array}{r} 7\,0\,+\,4 \\ -\ 3\,0\,+\,8 \end{array} = \begin{array}{r} 6\,0\,+\,1\,4 \\ -\ 3\,0\,+\ \ \,8 \\ \hline 3\,0\,+\ \ \,6\,=\,36 \end{array}$$

Now try these using the same method:

$$\begin{array}{r} 6\,6 \\ -\ 3\,7 \\ \hline \end{array}$$

$$\begin{array}{r} 5\,8 \\ -\ 3\,9 \\ \hline \end{array}$$

$$\begin{array}{r} 7\,0 \\ -\ 2\,8 \\ \hline \end{array}$$

$$\begin{array}{r} 5\,4 \\ -\ 2\,5 \\ \hline \end{array}$$

$$\begin{array}{r} 1\,0\,0 \\ -\ \ \,2\,8 \\ \hline \end{array}$$

Demonstrates the child's ability to calculate differences using regrouping (decomposition) within 100.

Using and applying
• *Follows instructions.*
• *Checks results and considers whether they are reasonable.*

Talk through the example on the sheet. Provide support or equipment (Base 10) if necessary. Assess the level of independence shown by the child (see below).

Note whether the child:
❑ works without support
❑ works without apparatus
❑ checks her/his work

Teacher comments

Teachers' notes, page 30

Name   *Date*

What's the difference? 5

Example:

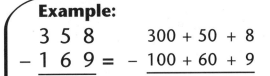

$$3\ 5\ 8 \qquad 300 + 50 + 8$$
$$-\ 1\ 6\ 9\ =\ -\ 100 + 60 + 9$$

$$\qquad\quad 300 + \ \ 40 \ +18 \qquad\quad 200 + 140 \ +18$$
$$=\ -\ 100 + \ \ 60 \ + 9 \ =\ -\ 100 + \ \ 60 \ + 9$$
$$\qquad\qquad\qquad\qquad\qquad\qquad\quad 100 + \ \ 80 \ + 9 \ = 189$$

Now try these using the same method:

$$8\ 2\ 8$$
$$-\ 2\ 8\ 9$$

$$4\ 3\ 6$$
$$-\ 3\ 4\ 7$$

$$6\ 7\ 7$$
$$-\ 3\ 7\ 9$$

$$7\ 0\ 6$$
$$-\ 4\ 3\ 8$$

$$1\ 0\ 0\ 0$$
$$-\ \ \ 7\ 8\ 6$$

Demonstrates the child's
ability to calculate
differences using
regrouping
(decomposition) within
1000.

Using and applying
• Follows instructions.
• Checks results and
considers whether they
are reasonable.

Talk through the example
on the sheet. Provide
support if necessary.
Assess the level of
independence shown by
the child (see below).

 Note whether the child:
❏ works without support
❏ works without
apparatus
❏ checks her/his work

Teacher comments

Teachers' notes, page 30

Name

Date

Countdown to zero

Teachers' notes, page 30

Demonstrates the child's understanding that the position of a digit indicates its value.

Using and applying
* *Uses a calculator to subtract.*
* *Applies an operation and checks the result.*

For each problem, ask the child to enter the start number into her/his calculator. The child should then change the start number to the next number in the sequence by subtracting the appropriate number and recording the operation. He/she should work down the sequence to zero.

Note whether the child can subtract:
❑ units
❑ tens
❑ hundreds
❑ thousands
❑ tens of thousands

Teacher comments

Start at | 1342
342
302
300
0

Start at | 7612
7012
7010
10
0

Start at | 12389
12380
12300
2300
300
0

Now make up your own:

Start at | ▢
▢
▢
▢
▢
▢

Name   Date

Keep on adding

From 0, aim for	in	adding (+)	multiplication (×)
50	10s	10 + 10 + 10 + 10 + 10	5 × 10 = 50
27	3s		
14	2s		
81	9s		
77	11s		
32	8s		
		7 + 7 + 7 + 7 + 7	
			6 × 6 = 36
	8s		5 × 8 = 40
45	9s		
	4s		8 × 4 = 32
54	6s		

Demonstrates that the child can use repeated addition and multiplication, and can see the link between the two operations.

Using and applying
• Uses flexible methods to find solutions.

Explain how the chart shows the link between repeated addition and multiplication. Ask the child to fill in the chart using the information provided.

Note whether the child can write:
❑ + facts
❑ × facts
for the same outcome

Teacher comments

Teachers' notes, page 31

Find the product 1

Demonstrates the child's
ability to multiply a two-
digit numbers by a single-
digit number.

Using and applying
• Sets problems for him/
herself.
• Follows a series of
instructions.

Work through the
example with the child.
Through discussion,
identify how the child
finds the product of a
single digit by a multiple
of 10. Note this in the
space below. Provide
additional paper as
required.

Note whether the child:
❑ works unaided

Method for finding
product of multiple of 10
and single digit:

Teacher comments

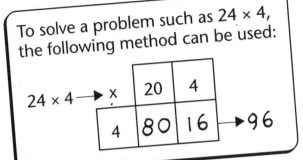

To solve a problem such as 24 × 4, the following method can be used:

$$24 \times 4 \rightarrow$$

×	20	4
4	80	16

$\rightarrow 96$

Try some examples of your own, multiplying a two-digit number by a one-digit number each time:

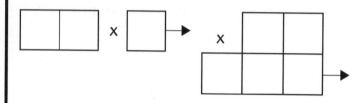

Teachers' notes, page 31

Name   *Date*

Find the product 2

To solve a problem such as 32 × 16, the following method can be used:

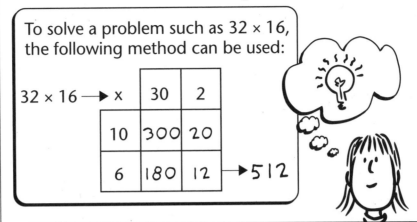

$32 \times 16 \longrightarrow$

x	30	2
10	300	20
6	180	12

$\longrightarrow 512$

Demonstrates the child's ability to multiply two two-digit numbers together.

Using and applying
• *Sets problems for her/himself.*
• *Follows a series of instructions.*

Work through the example with the child. Through discussion, identify how the child solves the multiplications involving tens and hundreds. Provide additional paper as required.

Note whether the child:
❏ works unaided

Method for finding products of multiples of ten:

Try some examples of your own, multiplying a two-digit number by another two-digit number each time:

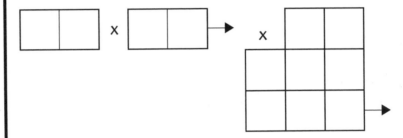

Teacher comments

Teachers' notes, page 31

Name   *Date*

Testing times! 1

×	5	3	2	4	10
6					
5		15			
4					
2					
3					
9					

Demonstrates the child's ability to recall or calculate multiplication facts involving times tables to 10 × 9.

Using and applying
• Develops own strategies.
• Finds ways of overcoming difficulties.
• Explains own reasoning.

The children should work in a group, with one copy each of the sheet and a stopclock for the group. Use the example (5 × 3) to clarify the procedure involved in completing the table. Time individual children's work (with a view to improvement in future attempts) to assess the speed and accuracy of their responses. Through discussion, help the child to answer the questions below the grid.

Note whether the child achieves:
❑ a high level of accuracy (27 or more correct answers)
❑ quick recall of all facts

Further work needed on:

How long did you take? (Add 15 seconds for every incorrect answer.)

Teacher comments

Which multiplication facts did you find difficult?

How did you work the difficult ones out?

Teachers' notes, page 32

Name _____ *Date* _____

Testing times! 2

Demonstrates the child's ability to recall or calculate multiplication facts involving times tables up to 9 × 9.

Using and applying
• *Develops own strategies.*
• *Finds ways of overcoming difficulties.*
• *Explains own reasoning.*

The children should work in a group, with one copy each of the sheet and a stopclock for the group. Use the example (4 × 4) to clarify the procedure involved in completing the table. Time individual children's work (with a view to improvement in future attempts) to assess the speed and accuracy of their responses. Through discussion, help the child to answer the questions below the grid.

Note whether the child achieves:
❏ a high level of accuracy (27 or more correct answers)
❏ quick recall of all facts

Further work needed on:

Teacher comments

×	6	4	9	7	8
6					
4		16			
3					
9					
2					
5					

How long did you take? (Add 15 seconds for every incorrect answer.)

Which multiplication facts did you find difficult?

How did you work the difficult ones out?

Teachers' notes, page 32

Name   *Date*

Testing times! 3

Demonstrates the child's ability to recall multiplication facts for given totals within 100.

Using and applying
- *Tries different approaches.*
- *Checks results.*
- *Works systematically.*

Discuss the task and refer to the two examples. Confirm that each section can have several entries. Encourage the child to find as many answers as possible. Observe how the child works through the task. Encourage the child to check her/his answers.

Note whether the child:
❑ works systematically
❑ shows accuracy (90% or more correct)
❑ checks her/his answers

Table facts needing further work:

Teacher comments

Write as many multiplication facts as you can in the second column. Each fact must involve two numbers up to 10 being multiplied together to make a total within the range given in the first column. Two examples have already been written in for you.

Total	Multiplication facts
Between 11 and 20	$8 \times 2 = 16$
Between 21 and 30	
Between 31 and 40	$6 \times 6 = 36$
Between 41 and 50	
Between 51 and 60	
Between 61 and 70	
Between 71 and 80	
Between 81 and 90	
Between 91 and 100	

Teachers' notes, page 32

Name

Date

Demonstrates the child's ability to find factors of numbers.

Using and applying
• *Selects appropriate materials.*
• *Selects appropriate mathematics.*
• *Investigates for a range of numbers.*

Discuss the example shown and allow the pupil to select resources for her/himself. Calculators can be used for this task if requested, but encourage the child to use mental strategies for speedy calculation. Record observations below.

Resources used:

Other comments:

Teacher comments

Number bugs

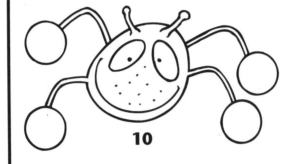

Number bugs have their factors on their feet.
An 8-bug has 4 feet:

Investigate some other number bugs, starting with a 10-bug:

Which of your bugs has the most legs? _____

Teachers' notes, page 32

Perfect bugs

Demonstrates the child's ability to apply knowledge of factors in the context of a practical challenge.

Using and applying
• *Selects appropriate mathematics.*
• *Selects appropriate materials.*
• *Follows instructions.*

Allow the child to select any practical resources (including calculators) to support her/his working. Question the child to identify the strategies used. Record observations below.

Resources used:

Comments:

Teacher comments

Number bugs have factors on their feet. A perfect number bug is one where all the factors of the number except itself have a total equal to that number.

Find the first two perfect number bugs. Both are below 30.

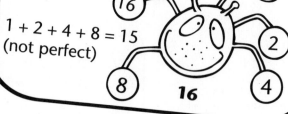

A 16-bug is **not** a perfect number bug, because the factors on its feet (16 excluded) do not add up to 16:

$1 + 2 + 4 + 8 = 15$
(not perfect)

Teachers' notes, page 33

Puzzling times

Investigate what happens if you multiply any single-digit number by itself and compare the answer with the product of the numbers one more and one less than that number.
For example, compare **7 × 7** with **6 (one less) × 8 (one more)**.

Demonstrates the child's ability to solve problems involving multiplication.

Using and applying
• *Identifies patterns and relationships.*
• *Solves problems using own or standard methods.*
• *Communicates findings in words.*

This task should be conducted without the aid of a calculator. If necessary, encourage the child to try multiplication involving double-digit numbers.

Note whether the child can:
❑ solve multiplications involving single digits
❑ solve multiplications involving double digits
❑ identify patterns and relationships

Teacher comments

What have you found out? _____

_____

_____

_____

_____

Teachers' notes, page 33

Square numbers 1

The first **square number** is 1. Shade in all the other square numbers featured on the grid:

1	2	3	4	5	6	7	8	9	10
11	12	13	14	15	16	17	18	19	20
21	22	23	24	25	26	27	28	29	30
31	32	33	34	35	36	37	38	39	40
41	42	43	44	45	46	47	48	49	50
51	52	53	54	55	56	57	58	59	60
61	62	63	64	65	66	67	68	69	70
71	72	73	74	75	76	77	78	79	80
81	82	83	84	85	86	87	88	89	90
91	92	93	94	95	96	97	98	99	100

Show below how you can find the **thirteenth** square number:

The thirteenth square number is

Demonstrates the child's knowledge of, and ability to generate, square numbers.

Using and applying
* *Selects appropriate mathematics.*
* *Understands the language of number.*
* *Develops own strategies.*
* *Recognises and extends the pattern.*

This task needs little introduction. Provide further paper (squared or plain) if necessary. If the child needs to be taught what a square number is, this fact needs to be noted so that a similar assessment can be tried at a later date.

Note whether the child:
❑ calculates the square numbers
❑ knows the square numbers
❑ uses pattern to predict 13th square number

Teacher comments

Teachers' notes, page 34

Square numbers 2

Use a calculator to find the decimal number which, when multiplied by itself, gives an answer as close to 20 as you can get.

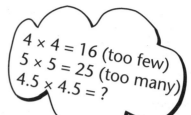

Demonstrates the child's ability to work flexibly with decimals.

Using and applying
- *Finds ways to solve a problem.*
- *Selects appropriate mathematics.*

The task should be carried out by the child without support from others. Examine the sequence of calculations to see whether approximations have been based sensibly on the previous attempts.

Note whether the child:
❑ works without support
❑ uses place value correctly for decimal fractions

Teacher comments

Teachers' notes, page 34

Name   *Date*

Cube numbers

Identify the number of unit cubes used in each of the following shapes:

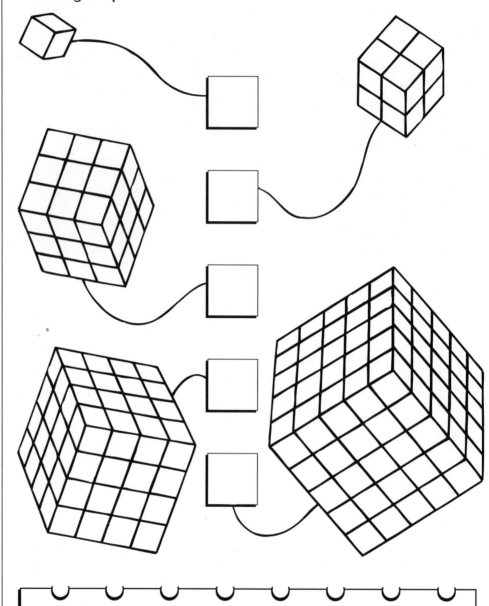

Demonstrates the child's ability to visualise and calculate cube numbers.

Using and applying
• *Develops own mathematical strategies.*
• *Presents results clearly.*

You should encourage the child to work without cubes, if appropriate. Ask the child whether he/she can say what a cube number is. Record a successful response in the assessment checklist below.

Note whether the child:
❑ works without practical materials
❑ works unaided
❑ knows the property of a cube number

Teacher comments

How many unit cubes would be needed for the next largest cube in this sequence? Show how you can work this out.

I would need _____ cubes.

Name _____ *Date* _____

Keep on taking away

Demonstrates that the child can use repeated subtraction and division, and can see the link between the two operations.

Using and applying
• *Uses flexible methods to find solutions.*

Explain how the chart shows the link between repeated subtraction and division. Check that the child understands that the answer to the division problem is the number of subtraction steps. Ask the child to fill in the chart, using the information provided.

Note whether the child can write:
❑ – facts
❑ ÷ facts
for the same outcome

Teacher comments

Go from ___ to 0	in	subtraction (−)	Division (÷)
60	10s	$60 - 10 - 10 - 10 - 10 - 10 - 10$	$60 \div 10 = 6$
55	11s		
42	7s		
48	8s		
30	5s		
28	4s		
		$16 - 4 - 4 - 4 - 4$	
			$27 \div 9 =$
			$25 \div 5 =$
15	3s		
	12s		$36 \div 12 =$

Teachers' notes, page 31

Mix and match

Demonstrates the child's
ability to use division
flexibly.

Using and applying
• *Finds ways to
overcome difficulties.*
• *Calculates using own
or taught methods.*
• *Uses trial and
improvement.*

Allow the child to select
appropriate resources,
but discourage the use of
calculators. Observe or
discuss the strategies
used. Note whether the
child uses trial and
improvement methods.

Note whether the child:
❏ works without support

Practical resources used:

Teacher comments

Cut the number tiles from the bottom of the page. Arrange them in the four statements below in such a way that all four statements are correct at the same time. When you have found the correct solutions, write them in place.

$$\square \div \square = 3 \qquad \square \div \square = 5$$

$$\square \div \square = 4 \qquad \square \div \square = 6$$

Now use the tiles to create another arrangement in which **all** four statements are different from those above.

$$\square \div \square = 3 \qquad \square \div \square = 5$$

$$\square \div \square = 4 \qquad \square \div \square = 6$$

Teachers' notes, page 35

3	6	15	20	24	4	18	5

Name _____   *Date* _____

Explaining how you did it 2

Demonstrates that the child can use flexible strategies to work out multiplication and division calculations.

Using and applying
• *Develops own strategies.*
• *Looks for ways to overcome difficulties.*
• *Explains methods used.*

Ask the child to complete each group of calculations. When the child completes each group, ask her/him to explain any methods he/she used to work out the calculations. Scribe for the child if necessary.

Note whether the child can recognise and use these strategies:
❑ doubling
❑ halving
❑ rounding up and down
❑ using known number facts

Teacher comments

$2 \times 32 =$

$44 \times 2 =$

$63 \times 2 =$

$2 \times 150 =$

_____
_____
_____
_____

_____
_____
_____
_____

$41 \div 2 =$

$140 \div 2 =$

$800 \div 2 =$

$72 \div 2 =$

$4 \times 99 =$

$24 \times 8 =$

$19 \times 5 =$

$21 \times 5 =$

_____
_____
_____
_____

_____
_____
_____
_____

$105 \div 2 =$

$48 \div 2 =$

$105 \div 5 =$

$800 \div 4 =$

Teachers' notes, page 29

Division One

A calculation such as 79 ÷ 3 may be worked out in several ways. For example:

or

$$20 + 6 = 26$$
$$3 \overline{\smash{)}79}$$
$$- \ 6\,0 \ (20 \times 3)$$
$$1\,9$$
$$- \ 1\,8 \ (6 \times 3)$$
$$1 \ (remainder)$$

$$10 + 10 + 6 = 26$$
$$3 \overline{\smash{)}79}$$
$$- \ 3\,0 \ (10 \times 3)$$
$$4\,9$$
$$- \ 3\,0 \ (10 \times 3)$$
$$1\,9$$
$$- \ 1\,8 \ (6 \times 3)$$
$$1 \ (remainder)$$

or

$$26 \ r \ 1$$
$$3 \overline{\smash{)}79}$$
$$3 \times 2 = 6$$
$$7 - 6 = 1$$
$$3 \times 6 = 18$$
$$19 - 18 = 1$$

Use **any** written method to calculate the following:

$$5 \overline{\smash{)}87} \qquad\qquad 3 \overline{\smash{)}95}$$

$$6 \overline{\smash{)}88} \qquad\qquad 2 \overline{\smash{)}97}$$

$$4 \overline{\smash{)}73} \qquad\qquad 8 \overline{\smash{)}99}$$

Create and solve some similar problems of your own on the back of this sheet.

Demonstrates the child's ability to divide a two-digit number by a single-digit number.

Using and applying
• *Selects appropriate mathematics.*
• *Devises and solves own problems.*
• *Follows a series of instructions.*

Discuss the three examples at the top of the page, demonstrating them on a blank sheet of paper if necessary. Allow the child a free choice of methods, but suggest that he/she try out all three methods (and perhaps others) to see which he/she finds most effective. Practical materials (such as tens and units blocks) can be provided if this helps. The child can also use a multiplication grid if necessary. Note any such aids in the checklist below.

Note whether the child:
❑ works without support
❑ calculates mentally

Resources used (if any):

Teacher comments

Teachers' notes, page 35

Name   *Date*

Premier Division

Demonstrates the child's
ability to divide a three-
digit number by a single-
digit number.

Using and applying
• *Selects appropriate
mathematics.*
• *Devises and solves own
problems.*
• *Follows a series of
instructions.*

Discuss the examples
shown at the top of the
page. Stress that there are
other ways of
approaching the same
question. Allow the child
a free choice of methods,
but suggest that he/she
try out all three methods
(and perhaps others) to
see which he/she finds
most effective. It is
unlikely that practical
materials will be helpful at
this stage. The child
should have a good grasp
of multiplication facts;
assess whether this is the
case through observation
and/or discussion.

Note whether the child:
❑ works without support
❑ calculates mentally

Teacher comments

A calculation such as
896 ÷ 4 may be
worked out in several
ways. For example:

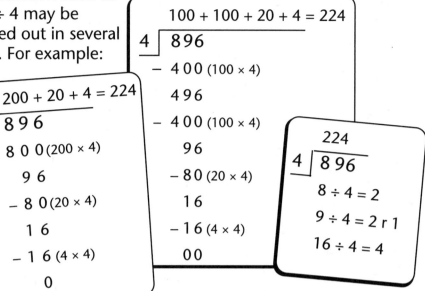

Use **any** written method to calculate the following:

3 ⟌ 363   2 ⟌ 690

3 ⟌ 728   4 ⟌ 915

5 ⟌ 996   4 ⟌ 666

Create and solve some similar problems of your own on the
back of this sheet.

Teachers' notes, page 35

Find four facts

Demonstrates that the child can manipulate numbers mentally. Demonstrates that the child can find number facts from available information.

Using and applying
- *Works flexibly.*
- *Works methodically.*

Ask the child to use each set of numbers to make four number sentences (see notes). Those in the first column should involve addition or subtraction, those in the second column multiplication or division. Ask the child to explain her/his methods and the relationships between the numbers.

Note whether the child can:
❑ find all the calculations
❑ explain the relationships between numbers

Teacher comments

+/−	×/÷

Teachers' notes, page 35

Name

Date

Fill in the gaps

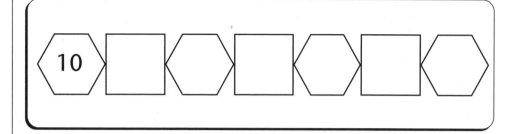

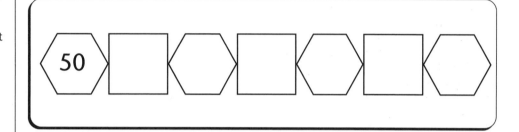

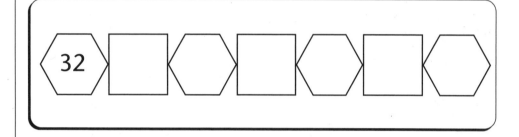

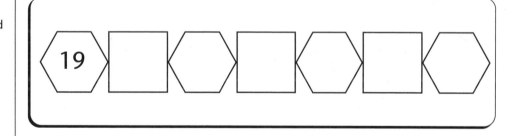

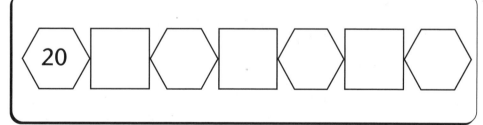

Demonstrates that the child can apply ×, + , − and ÷ operations mentally to numbers below 100.

Using and applying
- *Understands mathematical language.*
- *Works flexibly.*
- *Uses available information to work from.*

Explain to the child that you are going to read out some instructions (see Teachers' notes) for her/him to follow. The child should write down the instructions in the square boxes and the running totals in the hexagonal boxes for each square.

Note whether the child can use the following operations mentally with accuracy:
- ❑ ×
- ❑ ÷
- ❑ +
- ❑ −

Note whether the child can:
- ❑ record instructions and running totals correctly

Teacher comments

Teachers' notes, page 36

Name

Date

In my head 2

Teachers' notes, page 28

Demonstrates that the child can recall multiplication and division facts to ×/÷ 10 and use them mentally. Demonstrates that the child can recognise inverse operations.

Using and applying
• Works accurately.

Ask the child 30 multiplication and division questions orally (see Teachers' notes). The child should work these out mentally and write the answers in the boxes. After the task is completed, go through the answers to check them. Help the child to list (at the foot of the page) the ×/÷ facts he/she knows and the ones he/she needs to work on.

Note whether the child can recall and use:
❑ 2 ×
❑ 3 ×
❑ 4 ×
❑ 5 ×
❑ 10 ×
❑ ÷ 2
❑ ÷ 3
❑ ÷ 4
❑ ÷ 5
❑ ÷ 10

Note whether the child can:
❑ recognise inverse operations

Teacher comments

1.	2.	3.
4.	5.	6.
7.	8.	9.
10.	11.	12.
13.	14.	15.
16.	17.	18.
19.	20.	21.
22.	23.	24.
25.	26.	27.
28.	29.	30.

I know

I am working on

Name

Date

In my head 3

Demonstrates that the child can recall multiplication and division facts to ×/÷ 9 and use them mentally. Demonstrates that the child can and recognise inverse operations.

Using and applying
• *Works accurately.*

Ask the child 30 multiplication and division questions orally (see Teachers' notes). The child should work these out mentally and write the answers in the boxes. After the task is completed, go through the answers to check them. Help the child to list (at the foot of the page) the ×/÷ facts he/she knows and the ones he/she needs to work on.

Note whether the child can recall and use:
❑ 6 ×
❑ 7 ×
❑ 8 ×
❑ 9 ×
❑ ÷ 6
❑ ÷ 7
❑ ÷ 8
❑ ÷ 9

Note whether the child can:
❑ recognise inverse operations

Teacher comments

1.	2.	3.
4.	5.	6.
7.	8.	9.
10.	11.	12.
13.	14.	15.
16.	17.	18.
19.	20.	21.
22.	23.	24.
25.	26.	27.
28.	29.	30.

I know

I am working on

Teachers' notes, page 28

Name Date

Blank cheques 1

Demonstrates that the child can translate numbers in numerical form into number words. Demonstrates that the child can use place value in context.

Using and applying
- *Applies maths in real-life situations.*
- *Knows ways of recording.*

Explain (if necessary) the structure of a cheque: the spaces for date, payee, amount of money in words, amount of money in numerals and signature. Ask the child to read the amount of money in numerals on each cheque and write the same amount in words in the appropriate space.

Note whether the child can write amounts:
- ❑ in tens and units
- ❑ in hundreds
- ❑ in thousands

Note whether the child can:
- ❑ interpret the decimal point correctly

Teacher comments

Teachers' notes, page 37

Bank of Oak
Date
To:
£129.19
Bank of Oak
Date
To:
£301.10
Bank of Oak
Date
To:
£177.99
Bank of Oak
Date
To:
£1000.00
Bank of Oak
Date
To:
£1083.27

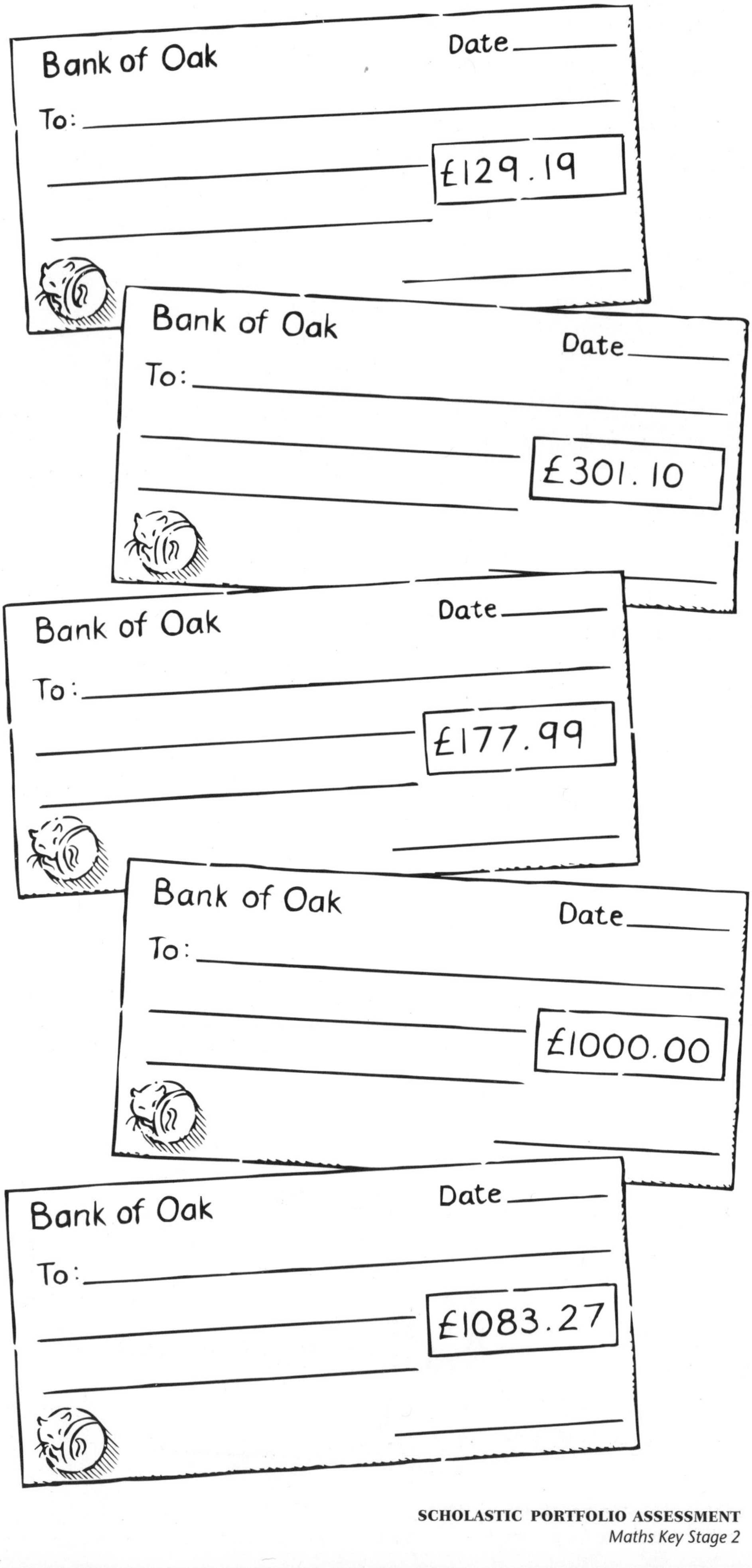

Name _____   Date _____

Blank cheques 2

Demonstrates that the child can read number words and write numerals. Demonstrates that the child can use place value and decimals in the context of money.

Using and applying
• *Applies maths in real-life situations.*
• *Knows ways of recording.*

If necessary, revise the structure of cheques (see previous activity). Ask the child to read the amount in words on each cheque, then write the same amount in numbers in the appropriate box.

Note whether the child can read amounts:
❑ in tens and units
❑ in hundreds
❑ in thousands

Note whether the children:
❑ use the decimal point in the context of money.

Teacher comments

Bank of Oak   Date _____

Two hundred pounds
and ninety-eight pence

Bank of Oak   Date _____

Three hundred and seventy-
four pounds and ten pence

Bank of Oak   Date _____

Eight hundred and eight
pounds and fifty pence

Bank of Oak   Date _____

One thousand three hundred
and forty pounds fifteen pence

Bank of Oak   Date _____

Five thousand two hundred
pounds and ninety-nine pence

Teachers' notes, page 37

Name   *Date*

European survey

As part of a European survey, the prices of identical items in different countries were compared. In which countries was the teddy bear cheapest and most expensive?

Demonstrates the child's ability to convert from one unit of currency to another.

Using and applying
• *Selects appropriate mathematics.*
• *Uses calculator and interprets results.*

Clarify the purpose and use of the exchange rate board shown on the sheet. Encourage the child to use a calculator, but do not tell her/him which operations are involved. Explain that the child needs convert each price into sterling, rounding up or down to the nearest pence (if necessary).

Note whether the child:
❑ uses a calculator
❑ calculates without support
❑ can round up/down to 2 decimal places

Other observations:

France 150 FF

Spain 3000 Pts

Germany 32 DM

England £12.50

EXCHANGE RATE [£]	
SPAIN	225 PTS
FRANCE	9.5 FF
GERMANY	2.75 DM

Teacher comments

Teachers' notes, page 37

Name   *Date*

Below zero

Demonstrates that the child can read negative numbers on a scale. Demonstrates that the child can apply +/– operations using a scale including negative numbers.

Using and applying
• *Applies maths in real-life situations.*
• *Understands and uses the language of number.*

Ask the child to use the thermometer scale to work out the answers to the problems. The problems are independent (not a sequence). Ask the child to make up her/his own problem at the end for another child to solve.

Note whether the child can:
❏ decide whether to add or subtract
❏ use the + and – number scale accurately
❏ work without reference to the scale

Teacher comments

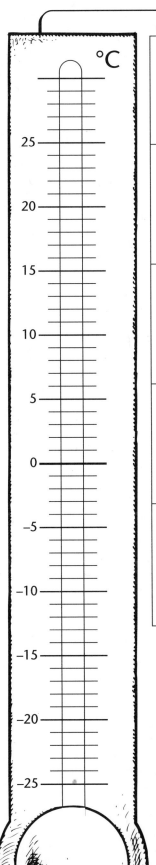

During the night the temperature went down 10°C.

It went from 5°C to _____.

When the sun rose, the temperature rose from –7°C to 10°C.

It went up _____°C.

In the morning the temperature was –1°C. By the afternoon it was 10°C.

It had gone up by _____°C.

The temperature dropped suddenly from 9°C to –3°C in three hours.

It dropped _____°C.

The highest temperature of the month was 11°C. The lowest was –8°C.

The range was _____°C.

My own temperature problem:

Teachers' notes, page 39

Real numbers

Demonstrates that the child can make estimates and gain a sense of the size of a large number.

Using and applying
- *Uses maths in real-life contexts.*
- *Collects information needed.*
- *Chooses appropriate operations.*

Ask the child to estimate answers to the questions on the sheet. Then ask the child to find the correct information from sources, experience and/ or calculations. Ask her/ him to note how the information was found. Finally, he/she should use the two blank rows to devise her/his own questions for another child to answer.

Note whether the child can:
- ❑ use secondary sources
- ❑ make appropriate calculations
- ❑ make sensible estimates

Teacher comments

Questions	My estimate	The actual number	How I found out
What is the population of the United Kingdom?			
What is the population of your town?			
How many children and adults are at your school?			
How many kilometres are there from Land's End to John O'Groats?			
How many minutes are there in this month?			

Teachers' notes, page 38

Name *Date*

Fractions 1

Demonstrates the child's ability to identify fractions of a whole, including equivalent fractions.

Using and applying
• *Uses diagrams.*
• *Selects and use appropriate mathematics.*

Explain that the sheet is subdivided into three distinct sections. Discuss the answers with the child when he/she has completed the sheet.

Note whether the child:
❑ recognises that equivalent fractional pieces are not necessarily congruent (see middle section)
❑ simplifies fractions (see final section)

Teacher comments

Shade in the given fraction of each shape:

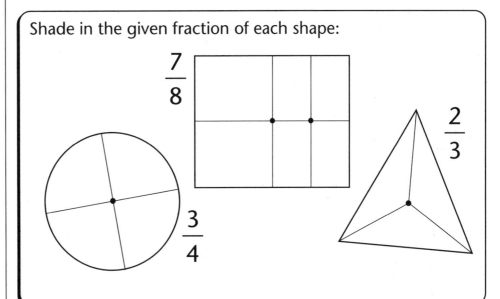

Shade **more** squares in each shape to show the given fractions:

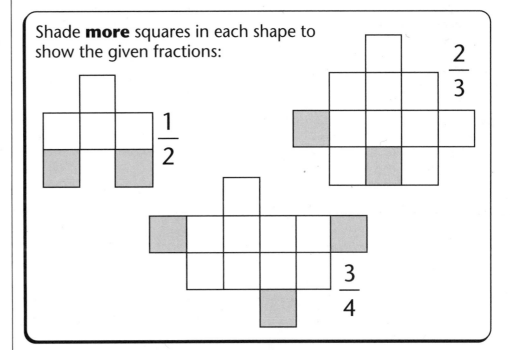

What fraction of each of these shapes is shaded?

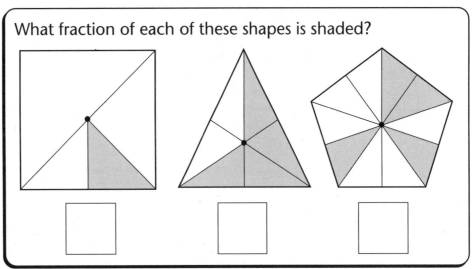

Teachers' notes, page 38

Name   *Date*

Fractions 2

Connect each fraction to its correct position on the number line.

Demonstrates the child's ability to order fractions on a number line.

Using and applying
* ***Takes increasing responsibility for work.***
* ***Devises own strategies for overcoming difficulties.***

Demonstrate how the fractions are connected to the number line using the example given $\frac{4}{4}$. Encourage the child to conduct any necessary working-out in the space provided. When the child has completed the task, discuss the strategies used.

Note whether the child:
❑ uses common denominators for comparison

Other strategies:

Teacher comments

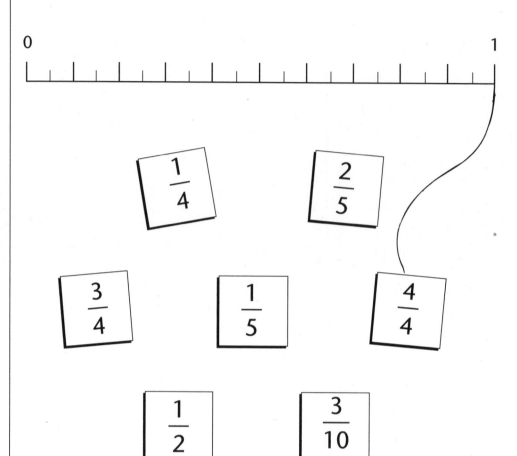

Do your working-out here.

Name _____ *Date* _____

Fractions 3

Demonstrates the child's ability to create and order fractions up to and beyond 1.

Using and applying
• *Works systematically.*
• *Takes increasing responsibility for a task.*

Ask the child to cut out the number cards from the bottom of the page. Encourage the child to find as many fractions as possible, including those which might have a value greater than 1. When the child has finished, ask whether all the possible fractions have been found.

Note whether the child:
❑ can order fractions below 1
❑ can order fractions greater than 1
❑ works systematically

Teacher comments

I made these fractions:

Arrange your fractions in order with the smallest first.

Teachers' notes, page 38

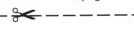

| 2 | 3 | 4 | 5 |

Name   *Date*

Fractions 4

Demonstrates the child's ability to calculate fractions of quantities.

Using and applying
• *Selects appropriate mathematics.*
• *Devises own questions.*
• *Uses a range of units of measure.*

Calculators should not be used for this task. Observe how the child works to assess her/his level of independence. Encourage the child to show all her/his working on the sheet. Discuss solutions when the sheet is completed.

Note whether the child:
❑ works independently
❑ simplifies fractions (where possible)
❑ can express a quantity greater than one as a fraction
❑ creates her/his own questions

Teacher comments

Calculate $\frac{1}{5}$ of 20.	Calculate $\frac{5}{6}$ of 90.	What fraction of £1 is 40p?
What fraction of £1 is 138p?	What fraction of 1 litre is 763ml?	What fraction of one day is 20 hours?

Write and answer some more questions involving fractions in the spaces below.

Percentages

Demonstrates the child's ability to work with percentages of a unit whole and of a quantity.

Using and applying
• *Selects appropriate mathematics.*
• *Applies knowledge in different contexts.*
• *Considers reasonableness of an answer.*

Calculators should not be made available for this assessment. Ask the child to show her/his working out for the second and third questions in the space provided. Encourage the child to talk about her/his methods. You may need to give an example of a solution to the final question, such as: 50% of 48 = 24.

Note whether the child understands:
❑ percentages of a unit whole
❑ percentages of a quantity
Note whether the child answers unaided:
❑ question 1
❑ question 2
❑ question 3
❑ question 4

Observations:

Teacher comments

Teachers' notes, page 38

1. Write some conversions of common fractions into percentages. One has been done for you.

$\frac{1}{2}$ 50%

2. Which of these three offers is the best, considering the original marked price?

£80

15% off marked price!

Special offer £10 off!

Hurry! Now only £66!

3. 40% of a class of 30 pupils are girls. How many boys are in the class?

4. Fill in the spaces in the statement below. Use the other side of this sheet to write more solutions, using different numbers in the spaces each time.

[ ] % of [ ] = 24

Name

Date

Spot the pattern

Demonstrates that the child can recognise a variety of number sequences involving addition and continue them forwards and backwards.

Using and applying
• Identifies and uses information needed to solve problem.
• Works mentally following pattern.

Ask the child to use each pattern fragment to complete the whole sequence both forwards and backwards. Ask the child to write what rule he/she followed on the line below.

Note whether the child can:
❏ identify the pattern
❏ describe the steps
❏ continue the pattern to completion
❏ work mentally

Teacher comments

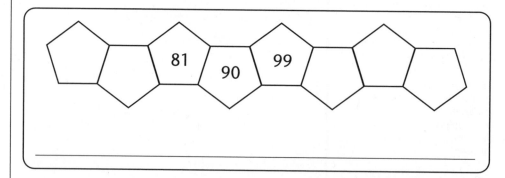

81 90 99

122 124
126

33 44 55

80 100 120

500 550 600

Teachers' notes, page 39

Name

Date

What did I do?

Demonstrates that the child can spot a rule and explain how it has been applied. Demonstrates that the child can work mentally.

Using and applying
• *Forms and checks own hypothesis.*
• *Explains own methods.*

Ask the child to look at each of these sets of numbers and work out what has been done to the first number in each pair to get to the second number. The same rule has been applied to each pair in a given set. The child should write down the operation in the speech bubble, or you can scribe the child's response.

Note whether the child can:
❑ recognise the operation
❑ explain how he/she worked it out

Teacher comments

How did you find out the answers?

_____

_____

_____

_____

Teachers' notes, page 39

Name *Date*

What comes later?

Demonstrates the child's ability to continue sequences and identify ordinal patterns.

Using and applying
• *Looks for patterns.*
• *Makes general statements.*
• *Makes predictions.*

Work alongside the child to complete the top sequence to the tenth term. Ask the child to work through all the other sequences, explaining the rule each time, and trying to predict the 100th term in the first three (simpler) cases.

Note whether the child:
❑ can continue sequences based on a generating rule
❑ can sometimes predict the nth term

Teacher comments

1st	2nd	3rd	4th	5th	6th	7th	8th	9th	10th
2	3	4	5						

The pattern goes up in ones. The number is always one more than its position in the sequence.

1st	2nd	3rd	4th	5th	6th	7th	8th	9th	10th
2	4	6	8						

_____

_____ 100th?

1st	2nd	3rd	4th	5th	6th	7th	8th	9th	10th
3	5	7	9						

_____

_____ 100th?

1st	2nd	3rd	4th	5th	6th	7th	8th	9th	10th
1	4	9	16						

_____

_____ 100th?

1st	2nd	3rd	4th	5th	6th	7th	8th	9th	10th
64	32	16	8						

_____

_____

1st	2nd	3rd	4th	5th	6th	7th	8th	9th	10th
1	2	3	5	8					

_____

_____

Make some number sequences of your own on the back of this sheet. Describe the pattern for each one, and predict the 100th term if you can.

Teachers' notes, page 39

Name

Date

Spot the rule

Investigate what happens when you add any set of three consecutive numbers.

$$1 + 2 + 3 = 6$$

$$\square + \square + \square = \square$$

Demonstrates the child's ability to spot a pattern and to generalise a rule in number.

Using and applying
• *Invents own examples.*
• *Recognises common features.*
• *Works systematically.*
• *Identifies a rule.*

Encourage the child to work with several sets of consecutive numbers, including some with large numbers. If the child finds it difficult to put ideas into words when answering the questions, discuss the child's observations and scribe conclusions for her/him.

Note whether the child:
❑ recognises common features of totals
❑ finds totals reliably
❑ recognises the rule for any three consecutive numbers

Teacher comments

What do all the different totals have in common?

_____

_____

Is there a connection between the middle number in the sequence and the total?

_____

_____

_____

Teachers' notes, page 40

Double trouble

Demonstrates the child's ability to double numbers mentally and using written methods.

Using and applying
• *Devises and refines own ways of recording.*
• *Develops own mathematical strategies.*

Stress the importance of both parts of the activity, the first part being purely mental. Discourage the child from amending her/his answer in the upper half of the sheet in the light of further work in the lower section. Talk to the child about the mental strategies used in arriving at the first answer. Ask the child how far the pattern continues.

Note whether the child:
❑ finds doubles mentally
❑ understands the notion of infinity

Mental methods used:

Teacher comments

Darren is starting at 1 and doubling the answer each time. Do the same yourself and see how far you can go without writing anything.

Double 1 is 2, double 2 is 4, double 4 is...

How far did *you* get?

Now use pencil and paper methods to calculate and write the sequence (below left). Use the space provided (below right) for working out your answers.

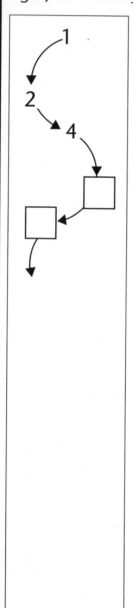

NUMBER

Input, output 1

Demonstrates the child's ability to represent a number relationship by a line in the first quadrant.

Using and applying
- *Draws a graph.*
- *Makes predictions.*
- *Looks for pattern in results.*

Talk the child through the function machine, the input/output matrix and the graph itself. The child needs to fill the input/output matrix with appropriate numbers for the graph. When the child has plotted these points, ask her/him to draw a line through them and answer the first question on the sheet. Ask the final question to see whether the child can visualise and/or explain the outcome for a different function.

Note whether the child:
❑ works independently
❑ checks results
❑ explains intercept on graph (first question)
❑ makes prediction (second question)

Teacher comments

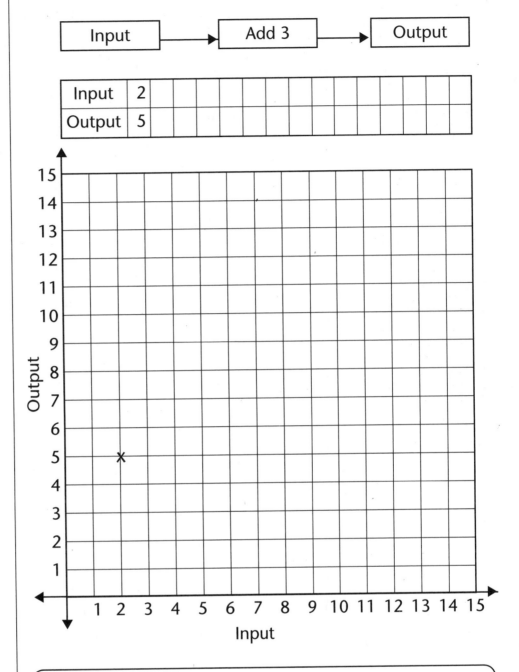

| Input | Add 3 | Output |

Input	2												
Output	5												

Why does the line cross the output axis where it does?

What would happen if the rule was changed to 'Subtract 3'?

Teachers' notes, page 40

Name _____ *Date* _____

Input, output 2

Demonstrates the child's ability to represent a number relationship by a line in the first quadrant.

Using and applying
• *Draws a graph.*
• *Checks results and considers whether they are reasonable.*
• *Looks for a pattern in results.*

Talk the child through the function machine, the input/output matrix and the graph itself. The child needs to fill the input/output matrix with appropriate numbers for the graph. When the child has plotted these points, ask her/him to say whether they look reasonable and whether they could be joined with a line. Ask the two questions on the sheet. Extend by asking the child to state the output for an input of 2.5.

Note whether the child:
❑ works independently
❑ checks results
❑ notes intercepts (first question)
❑ makes prediction (second question)

Teacher comments

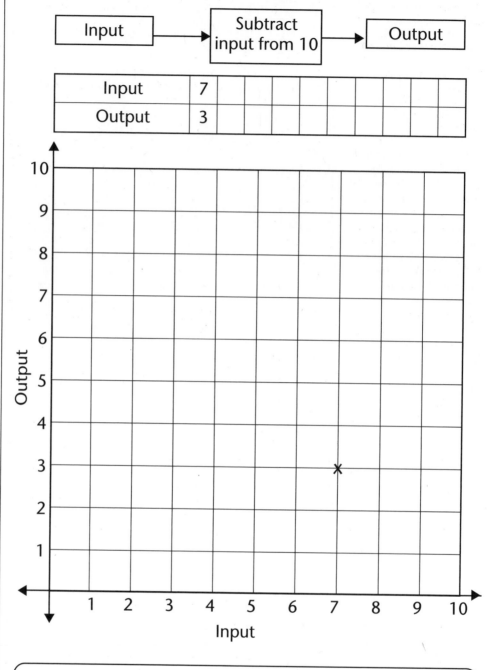

Input	7									
Output	3									

What do you notice about your graph?

What do you think would happen with inputs greater than 10?

Teachers' notes, page 40

Name   *Date*

Input, output 3

Demonstrates the child's ability to represent a number relationship by a line in the first quadrant.

Using and applying
- *Draws graphs.*
- *Checks results.*
- *Makes related predictions.*

Talk the child through the function machines and graphs. You may need to provide additional paper for the child to work out the input and output values prior to plotting the graphs. Talk through the questions at the bottom of the page.

Note whether the child:
❑ works independently
❑ explains differences
❑ makes predictions

Teacher comments

Use the two function machines below to generate two sets of ordered input/output pairs.

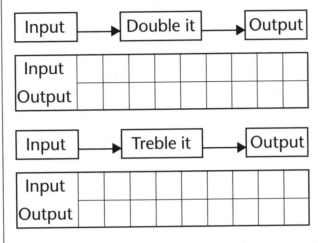

Input								
Output								

Input								
Output								

Record both of your sequences on the same graph below:

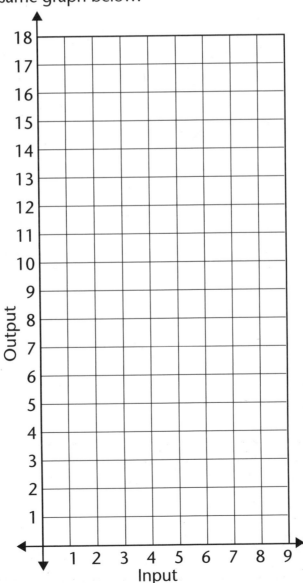

Use this space for working out the sets.

How would you describe the difference between the two lines you have drawn?

What would the graph of the function 'Halve it' look like?

Teachers' notes, page 40

Trampoline party

Demonstrates the child's ability to solve a problem involving several stages of calculation, in a practical context.

Using and applying
• *Interprets information given.*
• *Breaks tasks down into smaller routines.*
• *Organises work.*

Discourage the child from using a calculator. Make sure that all the child's calculations are written on the sheet.

Note whether the child:
❑ finds effective strategies for carrying out the task
❑ works independently of others

Teacher comments

The Sports Centre

((Why not have a sports party to celebrate your birthday?))

Trampoline party (max. 16)

• Cost of food and drink (per person) £2.75

• Hire of hall and equipment (includes qualified coach) ... £34

• Standard booking fee £3

Please phone for availability.

Use the information in the leaflet above to calculate the cost of arranging a party for 12 young people, including the food and drink, hall hire and the booking fee.

Show your working:

Name

Date

A sound deal

Find the prices of both an audio cassette and a compact disc using the information given below:

Demonstrates the child's ability to solve problems involving finding unknowns (in the context of money).

Using and applying
• *Finds ways to overcome difficulties.*
• *Presents work in an organised way.*
• *Uses logic.*

Discuss the information given, but do not suggest a method for calculating the cost of each item. Confirm that there is only one price for a CD and another price for a cassette. If the child works through this task with ease, let her/him investigate similar problems.

Note whether the child:
❑ works without teacher intervention or support
❑ works independently of others

Resources used (if any):

Teacher comments

Show **all** your working:

A cassette costs

A compact disc costs

Teachers' notes, page 41

Shopper's choice

Beach ball
£2.79

Pack of
cards
£3.60

Cassette
single
£2.49

CD single
£4.25

Three of the above items were purchased (only one of each item). Their total cost was between £8 and £9.

Demonstrates the child's ability to add up money and give change from £10.

Using and applying
• *Uses different approaches to overcome difficulties.*
• *Uses trial and improvement or other strategies.*
• *Explains reasoning.*

Apart from being given any necessary help with reading, the child should interpret the information and work through the task by her/himself. Money (real or plastic) can be provided if appropriate. As an extension, the child could identify the range of costs if **any** three items (one of each item) were selected.

Note whether the child:
❑ works without support
❑ uses money to aid calculation

Teacher comments

What items were bought and what was the total cost? Show your working.

The items bought were _____,

_____, and _____.

How much change is there from £10? Show your working or explain how you got the answer.

Change from £10: _____

Teachers' notes, page 41

Name   *Date*

Demonstrates the child's ability to use a calculator to solve a three-digit by two-digit multiplication problem involving unknowns.

Using and applying
• *Applies strategies of logic and/or trial and improvement.*
• *Uses calculators effectively.*

Observe the child to see whether particular strategies are being used. Encourage the child to record her/his attempts in order, so that you can review the work process at a later date. Consider whether both multiplication and division are being used.

Strategies used:
❏ trial and improvement
❏ logic
Operations used:
❏ multiplication
❏ division

Teacher comments

Find it!

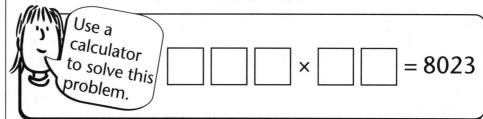

Use a calculator to solve this problem.

☐☐☐ × ☐☐ = 8023

Record your attempts below.

The solution is ☐ × ☐ = 8023

Teachers' notes, page 42

Round the block

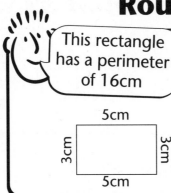

This rectangle has a perimeter of 16cm

5cm
3cm   3cm
5cm

Can you imagine some different rectangles with the same perimeter? Imagine (or draw on another sheet of paper) some rectangles of various lengths and widths, but with a perimeter of 16cm. Write the dimensions down in the table below.

Demonstrates the child's ability to explain patterns and relationships in a range of ways.

Using and applying
• *Looks for pattern.*
• *Makes general statements.*
• *Uses simple algebraic symbols.*

This sheet has three distinct sections: finding examples; describing a rule in words; expressing a formula using symbols. You may need to provide additional paper for a child who is unable to visualise examples of different rectangles.

Note whether the child:
❑ finds several correct examples
❑ works independently
❑ describes general rule
❑ provides suitable algebraic expression

Teacher comments

Length	Width	Perimeter
5cm	3cm	16cm
		16cm
		16cm
		16cm
		16cm
		16cm
		16cm
		16cm

Use words to describe a rule connecting the length and width of the rectangle to its perimeter:

The rectangle below has sides of length a and width b. Write a formula to express the perimeter in terms of a and b.

a

b

perimeter =

Name _____ Date _____

Nearest numbers

Demonstrates the child's ability to use number operations and understand mathematical language when solving problems.

Using and applying
• *Shows trial and improvement.*
• *Shows approximation skills.*
• *Finds ways of overcoming difficulties.*
• *Interprets and uses mathematical language.*

This assessment involves the child's interpretation of mathematical language, and any support given with this will mean that the checklist of words understood (below) cannot be ticked. Observe the strategies used and note any significant evidence.

Note whether the child understands the terms:
❑ consecutive
❑ as close as possible
❑ added
❑ twice
❑ total
❑ multiplied
❑ product

Strategies used:

Teacher comments

Find a set of five consecutive numbers which, when added together, give a total as close as possible to 74.

The set of numbers is ⬜ , ⬜ , ⬜ , ⬜ and ⬜

Find a pair of odd numbers which, when multiplied together, give a product as close as possible to 100.

The two odd numbers are ⬜ and ⬜

Find two numbers, one twice the value of the other, which multiply together to give a product as close as possible to 400.

The two numbers are ⬜ and ⬜

Find a set of three consecutive numbers which, when multiplied together, give a product as close as possible to 500.

The three numbers are ⬜ , ⬜ and ⬜

Teachers' notes, page 43

Name   Date

Hundreds and thousands

Demonstrates the child's ability to work with multiples of 10, recognising place value in the context of money.

Using and applying
• *Selects appropriate mathematics.*
• *Considers reasonableness of answer.*
• *Interprets results found.*
• *Uses maths in real-life contexts.*

Provide a calculator for this activity – in particular, it is necessary for the final question. Give help with reading if required.

Note whether the child:
❑ writes numbers in numerals (figures)
❑ writes numbers in words
❑ uses correct notation for recording money
❑ interprets calculator display correctly

Teacher comments

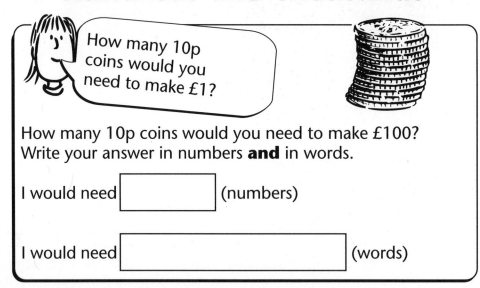

How many 10p coins would you need to make £1?

How many 10p coins would you need to make £100?
Write your answer in numbers **and** in words.

I would need [   ] (numbers)

I would need [   ] (words)

If one pack of biscuits costs 68 pence, how much would one hundred packs cost in total? Write your answer in two ways:

100 packs would cost [   ] (answer in pence)

100 packs would cost [   ] (answer in pounds)

Use a calculator to work out 1/5 of £9.00.

Write the answer that you see in the display. [   ]

What is the answer in pounds? [   ]

Teachers' notes, page 43

SCHOLASTIC
Portfolio
ASSESSMENT

DATA HANDLING

DATA HANDLING

The assessment activities in this chapter build on ideas introduced at Key Stage 1 (Primary 1–3), and also deal with the concepts of probability and averages. In broad terms, the activities in this chapter are made up of four significant elements: the collection and sorting of information; the representation and interpretation of information; the understanding and use of different types of average; and the use and application of probability.

Collecting, sorting, representing and interpreting data

The child's data handling capability at this stage should be characterised by an extension of graphical and tabular forms, and a growing awareness of 'fitness for purpose' according to the nature of the data and the anticipated audience. These representations place a greater demand on the child's understanding of the number system. A bar chart, for example, may feature a vertical axis which permits the reading of values in between the counting numbers. A pie chart often requires the conversion of a fractional quantity into an angular measurement.

In the years that follow, the child needs to be exposed to grouped data: information classified into a series of subsets and then used as the basis for representation. Throughout this time, crucially, graphical presentation needs to be supplemented with an interpretation of the outcomes.

AVERAGES

The child needs to experience, and appreciate the need for, the use of different kinds of average. The **mean** is the sum total of a set of outcomes divided by the number of outcomes in the set. The **mode** is the outcome which occurs most frequently in the set. The **median** is the central value in a list placed in numerical order; where there is no single central value (an even number of items), the mean of the central two items is calculated.

PROBABILITY

At an introductory level, this theme will require extensive discussion in order to establish a shared language of probability. Next, the idea that an event must be either *certain*, *uncertain* or *impossible* is an important logical step. A potential source of confusion here is the fact that while 'certain' and 'impossible' are absolute and fixed probability values, an 'uncertain' event can span the entire range of probability between these two extremes. Leading on from this is the introduction of a more specific vocabulary including terms such as *likely*, *evens* and *unlikely*.

The child also brings her/his own experience of probability to bear at this stage. Talking at home about a raffle, playing a game with dice and a range of everyday situations support the child's growing awareness of how probability is judged. Sometimes, however, these experiences can generate misconceptions: for example, children often come to believe that scoring a six on a standard dice is less likely than any other possible outcome. Such ideas need to be challenged through discussion and experimentation. Statistical work is typically introduced at this stage, so that the child can compare the results of experimentation with those anticipated through theoretical analysis.

Numerical values of probability are conventionally identified as being on a scale from 0 to 1 (inclusive), as shown in the diagram on the left. Work of this nature calls on relevant number skills such as the manipulation of fractions. The older and/or most able child can be introduced to the idea of calculating the probability of combined events – that is, of one particular outcome being followed by another.

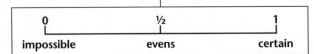

DATA HANDLING

TEACHING NOTES FOR INDIVIDUAL ACTIVITIES

Watching TV
page 124

Interpreting data from everyday life The questions on the sheet ask the child to find her/his way around the chart, make comparisons and calculate with the data. Record the child's chosen method of using the chart on the sheet. The second part of this assessment requires the child to devise four similar questions and answer a friend's questions. The clarity and accuracy of these questions and answers will indicate the child's confidence in using data presented in this form.

Yes or no?
page 125

Collecting and displaying data The child should be able to devise a question to which the answer must be yes or no. The easiest type would be a preference question such as 'Do you like cheese and onion crisps?' The child should then devise a method of carrying out the survey. This might be by asking for a show of hands, by ticking a list of names or by filling in a form with Yes and No columns. The child should then represent the data (in whatever form he/she chooses) and describe what he/she has found out. A child who has a good understanding of the process of collecting data will be able to pursue these steps competently and independently.

My own chart
page 126

Collecting and displaying data The child should choose a subject about which to gather data. You may wish to link this to work in other areas of the curriculum or activities in the school, so that there is a practical and relevant context for the collection of data. If you decide on several subjects with your class, you could collect the data quickly as a class, using class lists (for example, shoe size, eye colour, pets) and then ask each child to present the data. This will prevent the chaos of 30 children asking each other questions.

As this assessment is open-ended, your questioning of the child will be crucial. You should annotate the child's comments and note what the child does as he/she goes about planning the survey and presenting the data. At Key Stage 2 the child should be able to present such data clearly in a chart, working from a baseline. Some children may choose to make a square represent more than 1 person or object. Other children may realise that this would be a more sensible idea later, if the data will not fit on their chart. The child should label each group clearly and write a title which relates directly to the data. He/she should also be able to interpret what the data shows and answer questions that you pose about her/his method of presentation.

What colour is your car?
page 127

Using a chart where a unit represents more than one object This requires the child to interpret an arbitrary unit. He/she should understand that a half car does not have a fixed value: it may indicate any number from 1 to 19; for example, the number of blue cars lies between 61 and 79. Some may appreciate that it would thus be inappropriate for collecting exact data.

Pocket money
page 128

Collecting and presenting grouped discrete data You may prefer to amend the activity sheet by removing the graph (more difficult) or fully preparing the axes (easier). Figure 1 shows the solution. An able child will complete the graph with appropriate labels for the axes. The pocket money grouping (0–99p) establishes the range of each discrete grouping on the horizontal axis. A younger or less experienced child will need fully prepared axes.

Figure 1

Pie chart page 129

Representing data on a pie chart The pie chart can be graduated in advance by making marks around the circumference at suitable intervals (gaps of 12°, representing divisions of 1/30). However, this may undermine the assessment by over-simplifying the task. You may decide to allow the use of suitable computer software (for example, *Data Graph* from Topologika) in drawing the pie chart. Ask the child to input the data to the data handling package and use the printer to produce the chart.

The completed pie chart should be made up from sections as follows: Adventure 144°, Horror 72°, Humour 96°, Sports 48°. The more able child will appreciate that the angle for each category is derived from the fractional proportion. A younger child may need to be told what angle represents one person's choice (12°).

Averages page 130

Calculating mean, median and mode This task is appropriate to the top end of the expectation for Key Stage 2. Only the oldest and/or most able pupils are likely to have had the experience necessary to undertake the task. It would be appropriate to engage the child in discussion about the different types of average, and their applications, in advance of the assessment. Deriving the information from a graph rather than from 'raw' data adds to the complexity of the task. The solutions are as follows: mean shoe size = 2.1; median = 2; mode = 2. (See page 120 for definitions of these terms.)

Computer database page 131

Using a computer database Although it is designed as a generic sheet for use with most basic databases, this sheet may need some adaptation to suit your school's adopted software.

At the most basic level, a child should be able to enter data into a prepared file. In most cases, this requires the use of the Enter or Return key and/or the arrow keys, as well as the letters for the appropriate responses. With increasing familiarity, the child should be able to amend files and load/save work. At this stage, a child may be able to ask the computer a simple question such as: 'How many boys have information on the database?' The most able child may prepare a database for her/him and ask questions about the information which involve a double sort, such as: 'How many girls have a height greater than 140cm?' Exceptionally, a child may prepare a file and proceed to ask questions which lead to general statements (such as 'Taller children tend to have larger hands').

Possibly, maybe page 132

Sorting statements as certain, uncertain or impossible When carrying out work on probability, there is a need to be sensitive to children's subjective ideas of certainty and the related emotional issues. A child may regard her/his next birthday as certain, though it is not in reality an absolute certainty; in such cases, the child's view should be accepted.

Some children may misunderstand the final task and write statements which relate to past events. The child may well find impossible statements (particularly those derived from absurd situations, such as 'I will grow three heads tomorrow' or 'I will eat a million bananas at lunchtime') easier to generate than uncertain or certain ones.

How likely? page 133

Creating statements based on likelihood This activity is designed to follow 'Possibly, maybe' (see page 132). The complexity of the task results from its open-endedness. Discussion with the child will reveal the extent of her/his understanding. The statement relating to evens, for example, should strictly relate to a 50% (or 'fifty-fifty') statistical chance. In some cases, the

child may interpret 'evens' in a far more general sense (for example, 'It will rain tomorrow'). Your assessment will thus need to establish the depth of the child's understanding and growing awareness of quantifiable statistical probability (as in dice outcomes).

What's the chance?
page 134

Quantifying probability values from 0 to 1 This task is designed to follow on from 'Possibly, maybe' (page 132) and 'How likely?' (page 133). The solutions are: scoring a total of 1 with two dice – 0; scoring 7 on a standard dice – 0; winning a prize draw entered by everyone in your class – about 1/30; picking the longest straw from a bundle of eight – 1/8; throwing heads on a coin twice in a row – ¼; selecting one of the six winning tickets from a bundle of 16 – 3/8; throwing an even number on a standard dice – ½; throwing heads on a coin – ½; scoring 1 or more on a standard dice – 1.

An able child will calculate numerical probabilities based on quantitative statistical data, as well as identifying the more extreme statements found at either end of the scale: 0 (impossible) and 1 (certain). It is expected that a child will typically be capable of calculating values on the probability scale by the end of Key Stage 2.

In the bag
page 135

Relating experimental frequency to theoretical probability A 'feely' bag containing cubes or counters is particularly suitable for this task. The theoretical probability is ¼; you would thus expect to pick red on 5 out of 20 occasions. If the experimental evidence does not agree with the predicted result, this is because the sample is a relatively small one. If the sample size were increased, there would be a tendency to move towards the theoretical probability (as long as the cubes were randomly selected).

Typically, a child at this level will have a knowledge of probability and hence be able to make an appropriate prediction. It is not typical, however, for a child to have an awareness of sampling errors at the level given in the solution above. You should establish, therefore, whether the child's understanding is based only on a mathematical grasp of calculating probabilities, or on a deeper understanding of the difference between experimental frequency and theoretical probability. At the more basic level, the child might say: 'It should be five red, but I was unlucky' or 'Maybe the bag wasn't shuffled enough, so it didn't come out red five times as it should have'. At a higher level of understanding, the child might say: 'You'd need to do the test more times to see if it balances out' or 'You don't always get the result you expect, even though it should be red once every four turns'.

Two coins
page 136

Relating experimental frequencies to theoretical probability
Typically, the '1 head, 1 tail' outcome should occur as frequently as the other two outcomes put together. This can be explained by looking at the 'probability space' or possible outcomes. Of the 4 equally likely outcomes (see below right), 1 head and 1 tail occurs in 2 out of 4 (½) cases.

Typically, the child is surprised by the relative imbalance between the different outcomes. The able child will soon rationalise this by seeing that HT and TH are distinct outcomes, each as likely as HH or TT. It is important, therefore, that the activity is discussed between you and the child. You may wish to steer the discussion towards the concept of equally likely outcomes – that is, the fact that the outcomes HH, HT, TH and TT all have the same probability. Given this understanding, it is then possible to quantify the probabilities in mathematical (fractional) terms.

	First coin	
	H	**T**
H	HH	TH
T	HT	TT

(Second coin — rows)

Name

Date

Watching TV

	WHAT THE NATION WATCHED							
	BBC1	millions	**BBC2**	millions	**ITV**	millions	**C4**	millions
1	Eastenders	14.43	This Life	4.23	Coronation Street	14.98	Brookside	5.38
2	Airport	10.18	Third Rock from the Sun	3.60	Emmerdale	10.58	Friends	5.15
3	National Lottery Live	9.25	Gardeners' World	3.52	Wycliffe	9.96	Countdown	3.39
4	Hostile Waters	8.56	The Travel Show	3.32	Inspector Morse	9.68	Frasier	3.05
5	Neighbours	8.24	Absolutely Fabulous	3.20	Undercover Customs	8.83	Roswell	2.75
6	Birds of a Feather	7.48	Ainsley's Barbecue Bible	2.91	The Bill	8.64	Cybill	2.51
7	Keeping Up Appearances	7.43	All Mod Cons	2.62	Home and Away	8.28	Hollyoaks	2.44
8	BUGS	7.06	Reunion	2.59	Wheel of Fortune	7.25	The Ricki Lake Show	2.37
9	Getting Even with Dad	6.79	Tracks	2.50	My Father the Hero	6.96	And Then There Was One	2.36
10	One Foot in the Grave	6.70	Steptoe and Son	2.39	Tarrant on TV	6.93	Jewels of the Desert	2.25

Source: Broadcasters' Audience Research Board (BARB), July 1997.

Look at this chart of viewing figures for one week in July 1997.

What was the most popular programme watched this week?

_____

How many more people watched *Eastenders* than *Neighbours*?

_____

What was the least popular programme in this list?

_____

How many people watched *Gardeners' World* and/or *The Travel Show*?

_____

My questions and answers:

Demonstrates that the child can interpret a table containing information from everyday life.

Using and applying
• *Applies maths in a real-life context.*
• *Selects appropriate mathematics.*
• *Uses IT appropriately.*

Ask the child to use the data given in the table to answer the questions that follow. Allow the children access to a calculator to work out their answers. Then ask the child to devise four questions about the table to ask a friend, and to record these (with her/his answers and the friend's answers) on the sheet.

Note whether the child can:
❏ interpret the data
❏ calculate using the data
❏ devise her/his own questions
❏ answer her/his own questions
❏ answer a friend's questions
❏ work with the figures mentally
❏ use a calculator appropriately

Teacher comments

Teachers' notes, page 121

Name Date

Yes or no?

My question was:

What I did to find out:

My results:

What I found out from the results:

Demonstrates that the child can collect data using a Yes/No survey and present this data in the form of a chart.

Using and applying
- *Presents information clearly.*
- *Interprets the information collected.*

Ask the child to devise a Yes/No question and use it to carry out a survey (either in the class or in the school). You will need to provide lots of extra paper and access to clipboards, display paper, squared paper and, perhaps, a computer. Ask the child to represent the data in an appropriate way, then write comments on it at the bottom of the sheet.

Note whether the child:
- ❑ devises an appropriate question
- ❑ uses it to collect data
- ❑ chooses an appropriate form of presentation

Teacher comments

Teachers' notes, page 121

Name

Date

My own chart

Demonstrates that the child can collect data and present it in the form of a chart.

Using and applying
• *Presents information clearly.*
• *Justifies method of presentation.*

Ask the child to collect data (see Teachers' notes) and present it in the form of a chart, then to explain her/his findings by writing on the sheet. When talking to the child, ask her/him to justify her/his method of presentation.

Note whether the child presents information using:
❑ a block graph
❑ a pie chart
❑ a computer software package
❑ other form of chart (specify)

Teacher comments

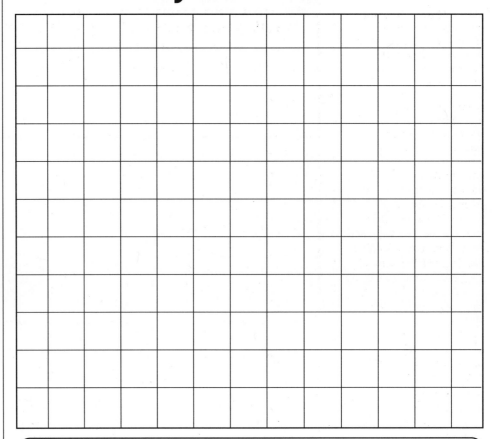

What I am going to find out about:

How I collected my information:

What my chart shows:

Teachers' notes, page 121

Name _____ *Date* _____

What colour is your car?

Demonstrates that the child can interpret and record on a graph where a unit stands for 20 objects, and interpret partial units.

Using and applying
• *Uses information provided to answer questions.*

Ask the child to use the data provided in the chart to answer the questions below. Then ask the child to show the numbers of white and gold cars on the second chart, using the car symbols.

Note whether the child can:
❑ interpret the symbols
❑ use the symbols
❑ explain the use of the 'half' symbol
❑ use the 'half' symbol correctly

Teacher comments

A survey was made of the colours of cars found in the local supermarket car park. This chart shows the most popular colours.

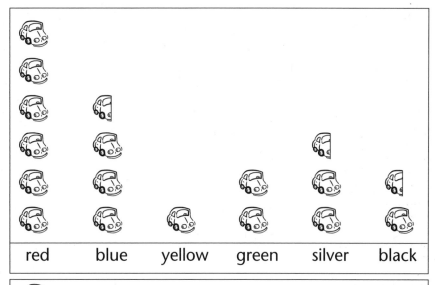

| red | blue | yellow | green | silver | black |

Each car symbol represents 20 cars in the survey.

Part of a car symbol represents 1 to 19 cars.

How many red cars were found? ☐

There were 40 cars of what colour?

_____

What is the largest number of blue cars that might have been found?

_____

What is the smallest number of blue cars that might have been found?

_____

How many black cars were found?

_____

| White (47) | Gold (23) |

Show how many cars, using the same symbols.

Teachers' notes, page 121

Name   *Date*

Demonstrates the child's ability to collect and present grouped data.

Using and applying
- *Presents information graphically.*
- *Selects appropriate mathematics.*

Talk through the activity sheet without giving any further guidance on the collation and presentation of results. Ask questions relating to the graph, such as 'What was the most common range of pocket money?' If appropriate, extend by asking the child to conduct a similar survey and present the results in graphical form.

Note whether the child can:
❏ choose appropriate intervals for sorting data
❏ perform accurate collation of data
❏ work independently

Teacher comments

Pocket money

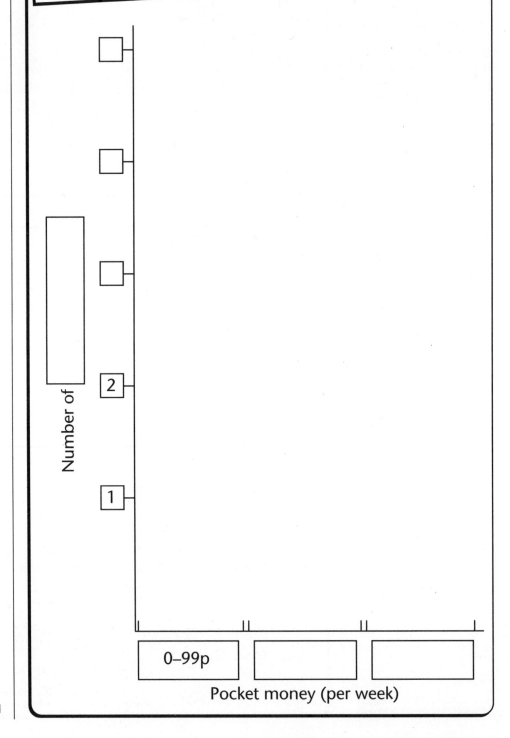

Dale £1.00	Julie 50p
Ashok £1.50	Chlöe £2.00
Steve 75p	Adam £2.75
Sara £1.25	Sinéad £1.75
Zöe £2.00	Jake 75p
Joe £1	Ish £2.50

The list above shows the weekly pocket money for 12 children in a class. Complete the graph headings and axes below, and present the results based on the information given.

Number of

2

1

0–99p

Pocket money (per week)

Teachers' notes, page 121

Name

Date

Pie chart

Demonstrates the child's
ability to represent data
using a pie chart.

Using and applying
• *Presents information in
diagrammatic form.*
• *Selects appropriate
mathematics.*

Provide spare paper and
calculators for working
out. Give the child a
protractor, but avoid
suggesting a particular
way to calculate the
relative proportions of the
four sections in the chart.
Retain the child's working
out, or talk to her/him
about how each of the
angles was calculated.
You may prefer to offer
this task as a computer-
based challenge (see
Teachers' notes).

Note whether the child:
❑ uses the protractor
correctly
❑ works without support

Method for calculating
angles:

A survey was conducted
with a class of 30 pupils
to find their favourite
types of fiction:

Adventure books	12
Horror stories	6
Humorous books	8
Sports stories	4

Draw a
pie chart
of the
results.

Teacher comments

Name _____   Date _____

Demonstrates the child's ability to calculate the mean, median and mode of a set of numbers.

Using and applying
• *Obtains information from a graph.*
• *Selects appropriate mathematics.*
• *Uses mathematical language.*

Leave the child to work independently on the task. Written presentation of results (including all working-out) is an essential part of this assessment, and needs to be emphasised. Discuss possible similar surveys (such as a survey of heights in the class) with the children.

Note whether the child:
❑ finds the mean
❑ finds the median
❑ finds the mode
❑ conducts her/his own survey (follow-up)

Teacher comments

Averages

A group of 10 pupils collected data on their shoe sizes. The results are shown in the graph.

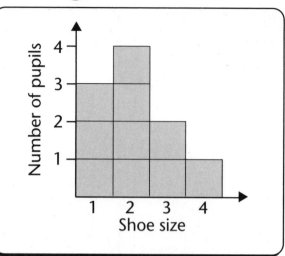

Use this information to calculate the **mean**, **median** and **mode** values. Show all your working-out.

Mean

Median

Mode

Conduct a similar survey of your own.

Name   *Date*

Computer database

Demonstrates the child's ability to use a computer database.

Using and applying
• *Can access and collect data.*
• *Uses computers.*

This sheet is applicable with most simple databases, allowing the child to record work done and show awareness of further possibilities. You may wish to add or amend some details before photocopying. Attach a printout (for example, a graph) if appropriate.

Note whether the child:
❏ enters information on a prepared database
❏ creates the database
❏ prints from the database
❏ can store/retrieve information
❏ can amend/add information
❏ can address questions to the database

Teacher comments

The computer database I used is called

_____

The database I have used contains information on

_____

I entered information on the following things:

_____   _____

_____   _____

What I can do with my database:

What I can find out from my database:

Teachers' notes, page 122

Name   Date

Possibly, maybe

Impossible	Uncertain	Certain

Demonstrates the child's ability to sort statements as being certain, uncertain or impossible.

Using and applying
• *Talks about the work.*
• *Extends task with own ideas.*

Ask the child to cut out the statement cards (including the blanks) at the bottom of the page, and then to sort the statements and stick them in place under the appropriate headings. Finally, ask the child to invent and write statements on the blank labels, and then to sort them and stick them in place on the sheet.

Note whether the child:
❑ understands the terms *certain*, *uncertain* and *impossible*

Teacher comments

Teachers' notes, page 122

You will be 10 on your next birthday.	Tomorrow will be Monday.	You will turn into a giraffe.
You will eat something later today.	You will get a telephone call later today.	Summer will follow spring.
You will win your next game.	It will rain tomorrow.	You will go to the moon next Sunday.

Name

Date

Demonstrates the child's ability to select events that have particular degrees of likelihood.

Using and applying
• Uses the language of probability.
• Begins to make general statements.

Ask the child to choose and write down an event that corresponds to each degree of likelihood. To start her/him off, discuss the types of statement which could go in the 'impossible' box (such as 'I will travel to the Sun'). When the child has completed the page, talk through some of the statements with her/him.

Note whether the child :
❑ can justify choice of statements
❑ correctly interprets the terms related to likelihood
❑ works independently

Teacher comments

Teachers' notes, page 122

How likely?

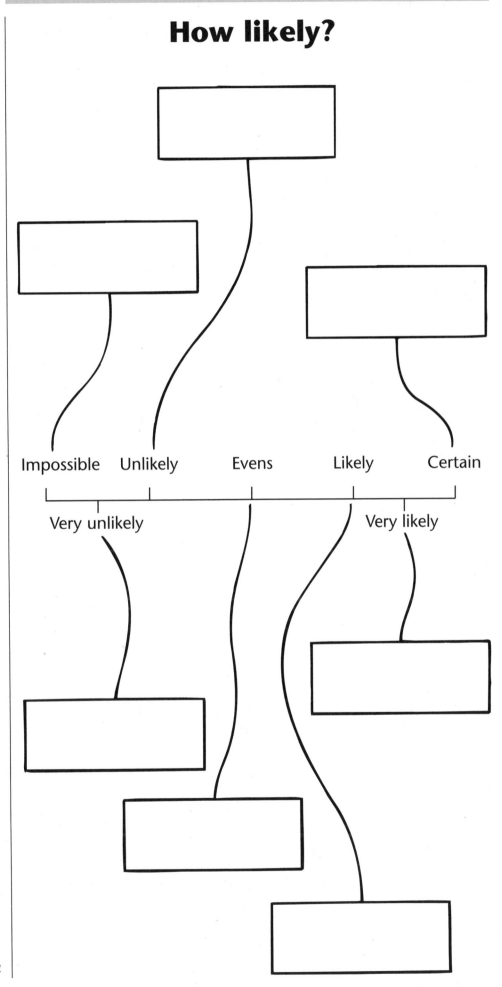

What's the chance?

Demonstrates the child's ability to quantify probability values from 0 to 1.

Using and applying
• *Explains reasoning.*
• *Selects appropriate mathematics.*

Explain that the nine statements are to be cut out and placed (and subsequently glued) in the appropriate positions to match the mappings on the vertical probability scale. Make sure that the child does not glue down any statements until he/ she has successfully placed them all on the diagram.

Note whether the child:
❑ works without support
❑ understands single event probabilities
❑ understands combined event probabilities

Teacher comments

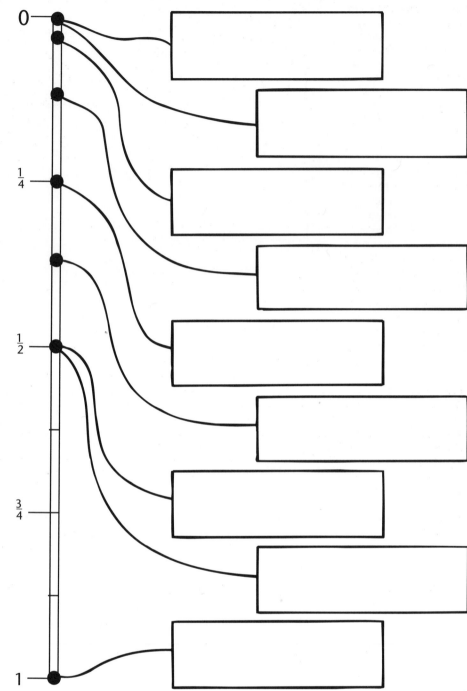

Teachers' notes, page 123

Throwing heads on a coin twice in a row.	Winning a prize draw entered by everyone in your class.	Scoring a total of 1 with two dice.
Scoring 1 or more on a standard dice.	Throwing heads on a coin.	Selecting one of the six winning tickets from a bundle of 16.
Scoring 7 on a standard dice.	Picking the longest straw from a bundle of eight.	Throwing an even number on a standard dice.

Name

Date

In the bag

If a bag contains 1 red and 3 white balls, what is the probability of picking a red ball out at random?

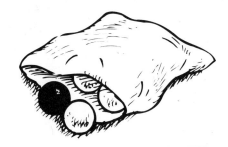

Demonstrates the child's ability to relate experimental frequency to theoretical probability.

Using and applying
• *Uses the language of probability.*
• *Obtains relevant information.*

Give the child appropriate equipment; let her/him carry out the experiment and complete the sheet. In order to make a full assessment of her/his understanding, you will need to talk to the child about her/his answers. The extension provides an opportunity for the child to develop her/his own line of enquiry, recording on a separate sheet of paper.

Note whether the child:
❏ talks about the work
❏ can calculate theoretical probability
❏ explains her/his experimental results
❏ explains her/his reasoning verbally

Teacher comments

Probability =

If the experiment was repeated 20 times, how many times would you expect to pick out a red ball?

In 20 turns, I would expect to pick red _____ times.

Try the experiment for yourself. Use beads, cubes or counters in a bag that you cannot see through.

Turn	1	2	3	4	5	6	7	8	9	10
Outcome (r or w)										

Turn	11	12	13	14	15	16	17	18	19	20
Outcome (r or w)										

Did the result match what you predicted? _____

If not, why not? What could you do to improve this?

_____

_____

_____

_____

_____

Design a probability experiment of your own with different numbers of items.

Teachers' notes, page 123

Name

Date

Demonstrates the child's
ability to find
experimental frequencies
and to explain them in
terms of theoretical
probability.

Using and applying
• Explains reasoning.
• Understands
probability.
• Uses the language of
probability correctly.

Provide the child with
two coins and let her/him
work through the sheet.
Discuss the experimental
outcomes (in the upper
section) and the
theoretical probabilities
(lower section). If other
children engage in the
task, encourage them to
combine their
experimental data and to
comment on the results.

Note whether the child:
❑ explains her/his
reasoning
❑ works without support

Teacher comments

Two coins

Throw a pair of coins 20 times. Record the outcome each time by putting a tally mark in the chart below:

Outcome														
2 heads														
2 tails														
1 head, 1 tail														

• Which outcome came up the most often?

_____

• Can you explain why this happened?

_____

_____

_____

• How often would you **expect** to get each outcome in 20 goes?

2 heads: ☐ out of 20 goes.

2 tails: ☐ out of 20 goes.

1 head and 1 tail: ☐ out of 20 goes.

If others are working on the same task, you might think about combining all the results.

SCHOLASTIC
Portfolio
ASSESSMENT

SHAPE & SPACE

SHAPE AND SPACE

This chapter presents activities to assess the child's command of the language of geometry, the properties of shapes in two and three dimensions and further work on reflective and rotational symmetry. It also provides tasks relevant to co-ordinates and the measurement of angles.

Vocabulary of shape and space

As in all areas of mathematics, the use of precise and unambiguous language is essential. At this stage, the child should be extending her/his knowledge of shape names and building a vocabulary of associated words in order to communicate ideas:

Shape names		Associated language		
Cuboid	Square-based pyramid	Faces	Similar	Congruent
Cone		Edges	Vertices	Translation
Cylinder	Pentagon	Curved	Interior angle	
Prism	Trapezium	Regular	Perimeter	

Because of the relative complexity of this language, the teacher's role in listening to how the child uses the language with peers in the activity, and in questioning the child after the task, is particularly important. For example, a child may have developed a misconception about the properties of a square. Such a child may identify a square by sight but not have a real appreciation of what makes it a square. It is only through direct questioning that the child's awareness can be exposed.

PROPERTIES OF SHAPES

Its geometrical properties are what allow us to give any shape a particular name. This area is fraught with potential confusion, for many reasons. Printed texts, for example, often imply categories of shape to be mutually exclusive. For example, the categories 'square', 'rectangle' and 'parallelogram' are shown in Figure 1. In reality, however, a square is a 'special case' of rectangle, which in turn is a 'special case' of parallelogram:

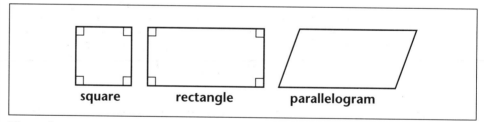

Figure 1

In order to classify a shape precisely, it is necessary to look at its properties and compare them with working definitions of particular shape families. To this end, a good-quality mathematical dictionary is highly recommended, since the issues extend well beyond the scope of this book. It is also important that the school has a consistent policy on the use of geometrical language, and a scheme of work which does not inadvertently promote common misconceptions.

Reflective and rotational symmetry

At this stage, the child needs to understand that a shape may have symmetry by virtue of its rotational qualities without having reflective symmetry. If prior experience has been confined to the latter aspect, it is easy for the child to associate symmetry only with mirrors. Figure 2 illustrates the distinction between the two types of symmetry.

Rotational symmetry is defined by a shape's **order of rotation**: the number of orientations at which it appears the same. A shape has rotational symmetry if its order of rotation is 2 or more.

A significant development from Key Stage 1 (Primary 1–3) is an expectation for the child to be more explicit about the mathematical qualities of symmetry – for example, being able to stage the 'order of rotation' or the point of rotation (axis) of a given shape.

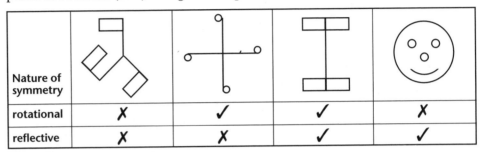

Nature of symmetry				
rotational	✗	✓	✓	✗
reflective	✗	✗	✓	✓

Figure 2

Position and movement

The assessment activities relevant to this area (pages 146-166) broadly encompass the following elements:
1. A pair of co-ordinates can be used to specify a location.
2. Shapes can be moved by means of reflection, rotation or translation.
3. An angle can be used to specify a measure of turn.
4. Networks and pathways can be used to describe movement from one point to another.

TEACHING NOTES FOR INDIVIDUAL ACTIVITIES

2D shapes
page 146

Describing the properties of 2D shapes While filling in the chart, the child should not have access to shape pictures or models, but should work using her/his own knowledge of shapes. This task also gives the child an opportunity to analyse the six given shapes in geometrical terms. At the beginning of Key Stage 2, the child should be able to complete this task confidently and accurately; it should provide a revision and confirmation of the shape knowledge learned in Key Stage 1. If the child finds reading the shape names difficult, read them aloud to her/him one at a time; indicate that this was done on the sheet, but take care to be sensitive to the feelings of the child. In such a case, it will be appropriate to scribe the child's responses.

Sort the shapes 1
page 147

Using geometrical language to sort shapes by their properties The child should demonstrate the ability to read and understand geometrical language, and use the properties described to sort the shapes. Each shape will only fit one of the sets, and should thus only be used once. The child should decide where the shapes fit best. A child whose experience is limited to regular shapes may find the irregular shapes in this task confusing; but it is important for the child to work with both regular and irregular shapes in a variety of orientations. If the child finds reading the criteria difficult, read them aloud to her/him one at a time; indicate that this was done on the sheet, but take care to be sensitive to the feelings of the child.

Drawing straws
page 148

Make and recognise quadrilaterals of different types Instead of straws, geostrips (in a similar ratio of length) could be used for this task. Having only two lengths of straw serves to restrict the variety of quadrilaterals made. Some of the possible shapes have specific names:

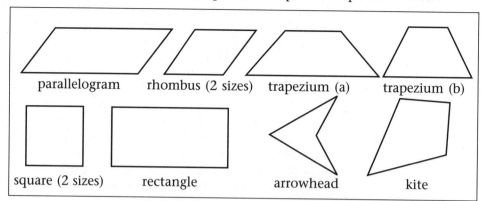

parallelogram   rhombus (2 sizes)   trapezium (a)   trapezium (b)

square (2 sizes)   rectangle   arrowhead   kite

The primary focus of this assessment is concerned with knowledge of shape names and properties. You might also question the child to see whether he/ she appreciates the mathematical significance of *similarity* – that is, where two figures have the same shape and angles but are of different sizes. A more open assessment can also be made of the child's approach to the task.

Typically, a child will find some of the shapes detailed above. A more able child will complete the task thoroughly, and will know the relevant shape names and properties. A child with less experience or awareness of shape may struggle with all but the most common shape names.

What's it called?
page 149

Recognising and naming 2D shapes If you prefer, reproduce the shapes as cut-outs and use name labels for matching. If you wish to assess the child's awareness of shapes without the aid of a word list, obscure this section of the activity sheet before photocopying. The solutions are shown in Figure 3.

Typically, a child will identify known shapes immediately and make an attempt at some or all of the other shapes based on the remaining words. A child who needs further reinforcement of shape may not immediately recognise the hexagon as such, due to its irregular nature. The more able child will need the challenge provided by removing the word list altogether.

Figure 3

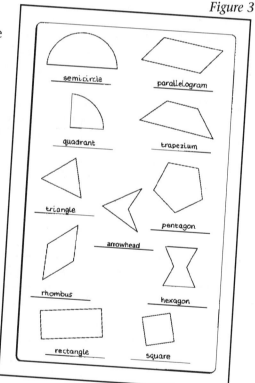

True or false?
page 150

Knowledge of 2D shapes and their properties You may prefer to change some or all of the statements for a child of higher or lower ability and experience. The solutions are as follows:

T	T	T
T	F	T
F	F	T
T	T	F

If you require clarification of some of the statements, a mathematical dictionary may be helpful. Several of the statements require a good knowledge of the properties of shapes. A child who considers a square to be outside the set of rectangles may have missed some of the interrelatedness of the types of quadrilaterals. A child who struggles with many of the statements will need more basic statements to work with, and further shape work will be necessary to identify some of the misconceptions that he/she has.

3D shapes
page 151

Describing the properties of 3D shapes This assessment is an extension of '2D shapes' (page 146). While filling in the chart, the child should not have access to pictures or models of these shapes, but should work using her/his own knowledge of shapes. This task also gives the child an opportunity to analyse the six given shapes in geometrical terms. At the beginning of Key Stage 2, the child should be able to complete this task confidently and accurately; it should provide a revision and confirmation of the shape knowledge learned during Key Stage 1. If the child finds reading the shape names difficult, read them aloud to her/him one at a time; indicate that this was done on the sheet, but take care to be sensitive to the feelings of the child. In such a case, it will be appropriate to scribe the child's responses.

The solutions are as follows: **cube** 8 vertices, 12 edges, 6 square surfaces; **cuboid** 8 vertices, 12 edges, 6 rectangular surfaces; **sphere** no vertices, no edges, 1 spherical surface; **cylinder** no vertices, 2 edges, 3 surfaces (2 circles, one curved rectangle); **square-based pyramid** 5 vertices, 8 edges, 5 surfaces (4 triangles, one square); **cone** 1 vertice, 1 edge, 2 surfaces (one circle, one cone).

Sort the shapes 2
page 152

Using geometrical language to sort shapes by their properties
Collect the following objects for the child to use in the task: a dice, a box shaped like a cube, a 35mm film pot, the inside of a kitchen roll, a tennis ball, a marble, a roll of sticky tape, a paperback book, a cone and a cuboid-shaped box. Alternatively, 3D wooden geometric shapes could be used. The child should demonstrate the ability to read and understand geometrical language, using the properties described to sort the shapes. Some of the shapes belong to more than one of the sets, and should be used in each set.

In order to record, you may wish to label each shape with a number or describe it by name. If the child finds reading the criteria difficult, read them aloud to her/him one at a time; indicate this was done on the sheet, but take care to be sensitive to the feelings of the child. In such a case, it will be appropriate to scribe the child's responses.

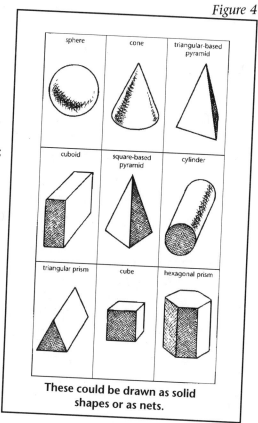

Figure 4

sphere · cone · triangular-based pyramid · cuboid · square-based pyramid · cylinder · triangular prism · cube · hexagonal prism

These could be drawn as solid shapes or as nets.

Shape designs
page 153

Recall and draw pictures of 3D shapes If the child is likely to have difficulty in visualising the shapes mentally, provide construction materials to allow modelling prior to drawing. While this assessment is not exclusively related to drawing ability, the drawn shapes should be recognisable (see Figure

4). If necessary, use discussion to ascertain whether the child appreciates the properties of the various shapes.

Typically, a child will be familiar with some of the more common shapes, but may find it problematic to recall the appearance of, say, a hexagonal prism. The most able child will be familiar with all the shapes and talk confidently about the number of edges, faces and vertices (or corners).

What's in a name?
page 154

Knowledge of 3D shape names and associated properties The shapes are a cube, a triangular prism, a square-based pyramid and a hexagonal prism. The table should be filled in as shown in Figure 5. In each case, the link between the faces, vertices and edges is as follows:
The sum of the number of faces and the number of vertices is two more than the number of edges or F + V = E + 2

Typically, a child will be familiar with cubes, pyramids and prisms, but may not identify the fourth example as a member of the family of prisms. A more able child will identify the link between the faces, vertices and edges. Such a child may even represent the link using a symbolic formula.

Name of shape	No. of faces	No. of vertices	No. of edges
cube	6	8	12
triangular prism	5	6	9
square-based pyramid	5	5	8
hexagonal prism	8	12	18

Figure 5

Describe the shapes
page 155

Using geometrical language to describe the properties of shapes In this assessment, the child is given the opportunity to use geometrical language to describe 2D and 3D shapes. If the child finds writing or spelling difficult, you might provide a list of terms to use as a reference, or scribe what the child tells you. Emphasise that the description should be exact enough to distinguish the shapes from each other and from other shapes. A child who can use geometrical terms with accuracy and understanding should be able to construct a clear and concise description of each shape. (Measurement of sides and angles is not necessary: what matters is identifying the properties of the particular **type** of shape.)

Draw the shape
page 156

Visualising shapes from written prompts The shapes are: a right-angled triangle; a regular hexagon; a cube; a cylinder. The child should try to visualise each shape before trying to draw it, to make sure that he/she has taken into account all the elements of the description. If you feel the child would respond better to hearing the description read aloud, you should do this and make a note of it on the sheet. By Key Stage 2, most children should understand the terms used (surface, side, vertice, straight/curved, right angle); but some may find it difficult to consider several of these in conjunction in order to visualise a shape. Let the child make several attempts at drawing each shape in order to refine her/his mental image of the shape.

Mirror symmetry
page 157

Creating shapes with symmetry Have suitable mirrors available for the child to use. Interlocking cubes could be used in place of the six cut-out squares, provided that you emphasise the 2D **outline** of the shape (not the 3D model) as the focus.

The use of six squares gives scope for a wide range of solutions as shown in Figure 6. Typically a child will find some of these solutions, and will identify

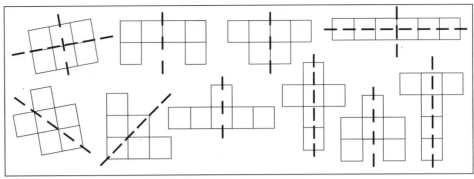

Figure 6

the mirror line in each case. A child who identifies the two shapes with
diagonal mirror lines (see bottom left-hand corner of Figure 6) is likely to

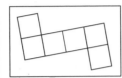

have a strong visual awareness of symmetry. A child
who suggests the shape in Figure 7 as having reflective
symmetry may need further work to rectify her/his
misconception (this shape has rotational symmetry, but
not line symmetry).

Figure 7

Lines of symmetry
page 158

**Making patterns using reflective
symmetry** This task should confirm that the
child entering Key Stage 2 can identify
reflective symmetry and check using a mirror.
(The sheet could also be used later, to check
the child's understanding.) The confident or
more able child should be able to find more
than one line of symmetry. Figure 8 shows all
the lines of symmetry which can be drawn on
these patterns. The two empty squares give
you the opportunity to assess whether the
child can create her/his own pattern involving reflective symmetry; the
complexity of the child's patterns will help to indicate her/his
understanding of this concept.

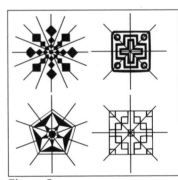

Figure 8

Rotational symmetry
page 159

**Identifying rotational
symmetry** Anticipate what
additional materials might be
requested. If the child has
previously used tracing paper as a
way of overlaying the original to
test for rotational properties, this
resource should be provided.

Figure 9 shows the order or
rotation for each of the shapes that
have rotational symmetry. The
most able or experienced child will
identify all the shapes with
rotational symmetry, and may also
detail both the order of rotation
and the point about which each
shape rotates. Typically, a child
should find ways to test for
rotational symmetry, perhaps by
using tracing paper or simply by
rotating the page. A child who
has difficulty with this concept

Figure 9

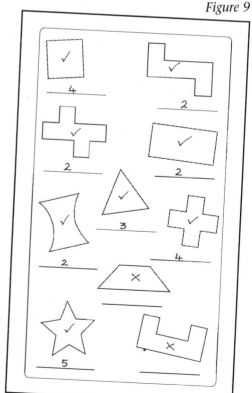

may need to be taken through the task with a significant amount of adult support.

Angle 1
page 160

Estimating and measuring angles The angles in the four illustrated examples are as follows: 65°, 135°, 35°, 320°. The child's 'acute' and 'obtuse' angles should be between 0° and 90°, and between 90° and 180° respectively.

Make available angle measuring instruments with which the child is familiar. A child may find accurate use of a protractor somewhat problematic. You should allow 2° to 3° tolerance (either way) under measurement. (Note that the printing process, as well as subsequent photocopying distortions, may lead the illustrations to be very slightly different from the answers given above.) A child confident with shape work will use the protractor effectively, will need no clarification of the terms 'acute' and 'obtuse' and may be familiar with the concept of a 'reflex' angle.

Angle 2
page 161

Calculating external angles of regular polygons This task lends itself to computer applications (such as Logo) or programmable vehicles with an angle facility (such as PIP or Roamer). Alternatively, you might provide large sheets of blank paper for the child to draw the shapes. If the child is using a computer or programmable vehicle, you might expect a small degree of error. Small variations in the surface used with a programmable vehicle, for example, can make a significant difference to its performance.

Typically, a child will arrive at or near a satisfactory solution using trial and improvement methods with pencil and paper. The more able child may recognise the link between the external angle and the need to turn through 360° overall. By reasoning in this way, the external angle for a regular octagon can be worked out as 1/8th of 360°, that is, 45°.

Angle 3
page 162

Identifying relationships involving external and internal angles It is important for the child to have had some degree of success with the 'Angle 2' activity (page 161) before undertaking this task. Figure 10 shows the correct figures in the table.

This is a complex activity, designed for the older and/or more confident child. Such a child may observe that the sum of the internal angles gets larger as the number of sides increases, while the sum of the external angles remains constant at 360°.

Figure 10	Equilateral triangle	Square	Regular pentagon	Regular hexagon
Internal angle	60°	90°	108°	120°
No. of sides	3	4	5	6
Sum of internal angles	180°	360°	540°	720°
External angle	120°	90°	72°	60°
No. of external angles	3	4	5	6
Sum of external angles	360°	360°	360°	360°

Nets of shapes
page 163

Modelling and visualising nets of cubes Commercial construction materials (such as Polydron or Clixi) are ideal for this activity. The task offers many solutions, including those shown in Figure 11. *Figure 11*

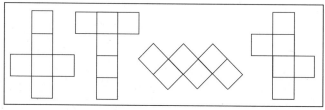

Most children will have some degree of success with this activity. The more able child will find new arrangements based on earlier successful attempts – for example, by moving one piece only. A less able child may repeat her/himself, not realising that some apparently new solutions are only rotations of others. Such a child may also start from scratch each time, not making use of previous solutions to generate new ones.

Area and perimeter
page 164

Investigating relationships between area and perimeter
Interlocking plastic squares (such as Polydron) could be used for this task. The minimum perimeter for the four squares is 8 unit lengths, with the squares arranged in a larger square. The maximum perimeter is 10 unit lengths, as in the example given on the photocopiable sheet.

Typically, a child will have some success in finding the perimeter for specific arrangements. An able child will work methodically and will begin to identify that the minimum perimeter is created by 'clumping' the squares together in a square block. In exceptional cases, a child will find a general rule for any number of squares (n):
maximum perimeter for n squares = 2n + 2

Same area, different shape
page 165

Calculating area by adding whole and part squares
Figure 12 shows some examples of satisfactory solutions. An able child might arrive at successful solutions using an awareness of basic formulae. The illustrated triangle, for example, features two sides of length 8 and 3 units: the hypotenuse essentially halves what would have been an 8 × 3 rectangle, and thus the triangle has an area of 12 square units. Typically, a child will have some success finding correct shapes. A less experienced or less able child will have problems counting part squares, and may become frustrated by unsuccessful attempts.

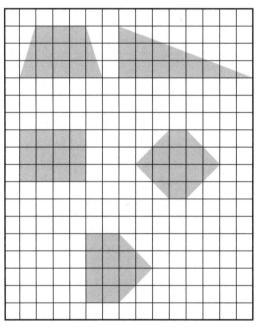

Figure 12

Enlargement
page 166

Enlarging shapes by a scale factor of 2 or greater Typically, a child will be able to identify the co-ordinates given at the top of the page and represent these as points on the grid. In doubling and tripling, the child should appreciate the need to avoid confusing x and y co-ordinates. The more able child will recognise that enlarging by scale factors of 2 and 3 increase the area by 4 and 9 respectively, and may even use this to predict

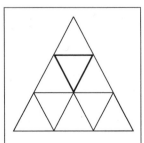

that a scale factor of 4 will have the effect of making the area 16 times greater than the original. Although counting squares is one method of calculating area, the different parts of squares covered by these shapes makes it difficult to add up the squares accurately. A more effective method is to visualise fitting several of the smaller shapes into the larger (similar) shape, as shown in Figure 13.

Figure 13

Name   Date

2D shapes

Demonstrates that the child can draw and describe the properties of basic 2D shapes.

Using and applying
• Uses specific geometrical language.
• Uses everyday experiences in a mathematical context.

Ask the child to complete the chart, working across all the columns. The first column should be filled in with drawings, the others with writing. In the final column, the child should note other observations about the properties of the shapes.

Note whether the child can draw and describe:
❑ triangles
❑ squares
❑ rectangles
❑ pentagons
❑ circles
❑ hexagons

Teacher comments

Picture of the shape	Name of the shape	Number of corners	Number of sides	Other things I have noticed
	triangle			
	square			
	rectangle			
	pentagon			
	circle			
	hexagon			

Teachers' notes, page 139

Name

Date

Sort the shapes 1

Demonstrates that the child can use the properties of 2D shapes to classify and identify them.

Demonstrates that the child recognises regular and irregular shapes.

Using and applying
• *Works methodically.*

Ask the child to cut out the shape pictures at the bottom of the page. The child should then sort the shapes into the appropriate sets, reading the criteria carefully. When the child is sure that the sorting is correct, he/she should stick down the shapes in place on the sheet. Through questioning, establish whether the child can distinguish between regular and irregular shapes, naming the regular shapes.

Teacher comments

Shapes with no straight sides

Shapes with 3 or 4 straight sides

Shapes with more than 4 straight sides

Teachers' notes, page 139

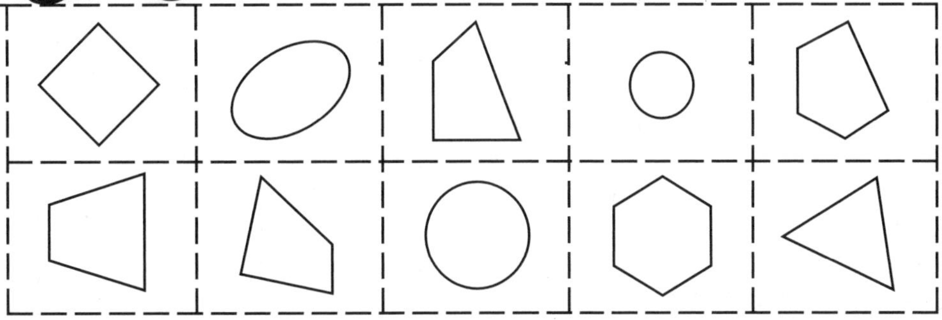

Name

Date

Drawing straws

You need lots of straws in two different lengths.

How many different **types of quadrilateral** can you make and draw? Do any of them have special names?

Demonstrates the child's ability to make and identify quadrilaterals of different types.

Using and applying
• *Works systematically.*
• *Knows names of shapes.*
• *Records work pictorially.*

Provide a bundle of straws in two different lengths (ideally 10cm and 7cm, in two contrasting colours). Read the instructions to the child. When he/she has finished, read the final question on the sheet to the child. Make sure that he/she understands the idea of the different types (categories) of quadrilateral.

Note whether the child:
❑ identifies types of quadrilateral
❑ works methodically

Teacher comments

Have you found them all?

Teachers' notes, page 139

Demonstrates the child's ability to recognise and name 2D shapes.

Using and applying
• *Talks about properties of shapes.*
• *Uses mathematically precise language.*

Draw the child's attention to the word list at the top of the page, and the completed example. As the child is working through the task, discuss some of the completed labels with her/him in order to ascertain whether the child can describe these shapes in relation to their mathematical properties.

Note whether the child can:
❏ label shapes correctly
❏ talk about properties of shapes

Properties discussed:

Teacher comments

Teachers' notes, page 140

What's it called?

Write the correct name alongside each of the shapes below. One has been done for you.

> arrowhead, quadrant, triangle, pentagon, parallelogram, semicircle, trapezium, hexagon, rhombus, rectangle, square

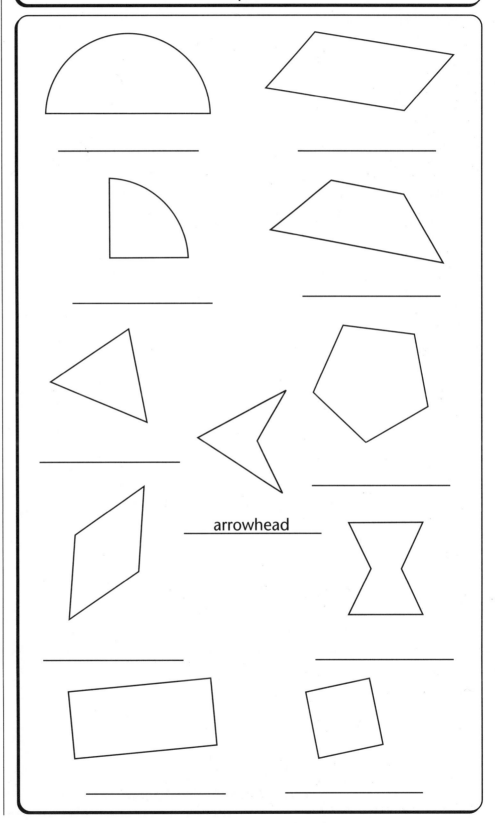

arrowhead

Demonstrates the child's knowledge of 2D shapes and their properties.

Using and applying
- *Analyses and considers mathematical statements.*
- *Justifies decisions.*
- *Uses mathematically precise vocabulary.*

As the child is working through the task, ask her/him to give a reason for each decision. Encourage the child to classify all of the statements before sticking any of them down.

Note whether the child can:
❑ work independently of others
❑ work without teacher support
❑ give reasons for decisions (verbally)

Teacher comments

Teachers' notes, page 140

✂ - - - - - - - - - - - -

Name _____   Date _____

True or false?

Cut out the labels at the bottom of the page. Stick each one in the right section of this table:

True ✓	False ✗

All squares are rectangles.	A square has 4 lines of symmetry.	A rhombus is a parallelogram.
An acute angle is less than 90°.	No pentagons tessellate.	The sum of the angles in a triangle is 180°
A rectangle is a regular shape.	All hexagons are symmetrical.	A polygon *must* have straight sides.
All quadrilaterals have 4 sides.	A pentagon has 5 sides.	All rectangles have 4 lines of symmetry.

Name

Date

3D shapes

Demonstrates that the
child can name 3D
shapes and describe their
properties.

Using and applying
* *Uses specific
geometrical language.*
* *Uses everyday
experiences in a
mathematical context.*

Ask the child to complete
the chart, working across
each row. The final
column should be used
by the child to record
other observations about
the properties of the
shapes.

*Note whether the child
can use precise
mathematical vocabulary
to describe the properties
of:*
❑ a cube
❑ a cuboid
❑ a sphere
❑ a cylinder
❑ a square-based
pyramid
❑ a cone

Teacher comments

Name and picture of shape	Number of vertices	Number of edges	Number and shapes of surfaces	Other things I have noticed
cube				
cuboid				
sphere				
cylinder				
square-based pyramid				
cone				

Teachers' notes, page 141

Name

Date

Sort the shapes 2

Demonstrates that the
child can use the
properties of 3D shapes to
classify them.
Demonstrates that the
child can recognise both
regular and irregular
shapes.

Using and applying
• Works methodically.

Provide the objects listed
in the Teacher's notes. Ask
the child to sort these
shapes into the four sets,
reading all the criteria
carefully. Then ask the
child to record the sorting
by drawing the shapes or
writing their names. Each
shape can be placed in
more than one set.

Teacher comments

Shapes
with 1, 2
or 3
surfaces

Shapes
with 8
corners

Shapes
that roll

Shapes
with both
flat and
curved
surfaces

Teachers' notes, page 141

Name

Date

Shape designs

Draw each of the following shapes. The first one has been done for you.

Demonstrates the child's ability to recall and draw correct pictures of 3D shapes.

Using and applying
• *Has knowledge of shape names and properties.*
• *Talks about the work.*

Give the child a choice between drawing either solid or skeletal representations of the shapes. If necessary, provide construction straws (or similar commercial kits) for the child to model the shapes first. Encourage the child to talk about the properties of some of the shapes in relation to how they are drawn.

Note whether the child:
❑ works independently of others
❑ works without teacher support

Relevant vocabulary used:

Teacher comments

sphere 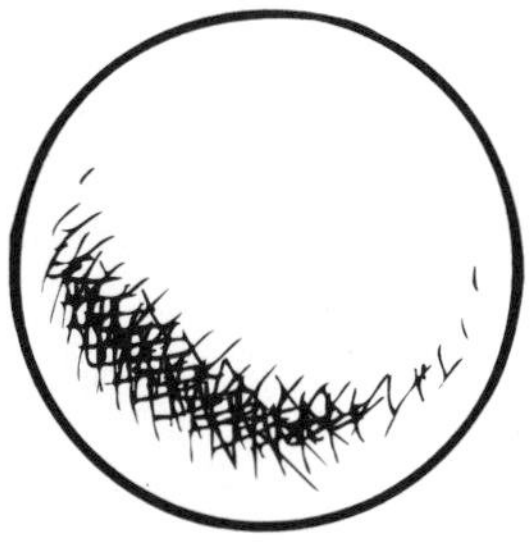	cone	triangular-based pyramid
cuboid	square-based pyramid	cylinder
triangular prism	cube	hexagonal prism

Teachers' notes, page 141

Name _____   *Date* _____

Demonstrates the child's
knowledge of 3D shape
names and associated
properties. Demonstrates
the child's knowledge of
geometrical vocabulary.

Using and applying
• *Knows and uses
mathematical vocabulary.*
• *Identifies patterns and
relationships.*

Draw the child's attention
to the three sections of
the activity sheet. If some
names of shapes have to
be given to the child,
code the boxes as such to
aid future analysis (eg 'T'
for 'told'). If the child
identifies a link in the final
task, encourage her/him
to write it symbolically
using letters and
numerals.

Note whether the child:
❑ works independently
of others
❑ works without teacher
support
❑ identifies relationship
between numbers of
faces, vertices, and edges

Teacher comments

What's in a name?

Name each of the following shapes.

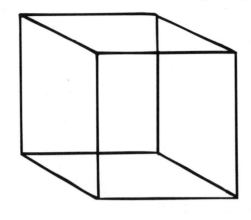

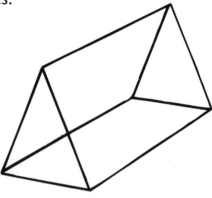

_____   _____

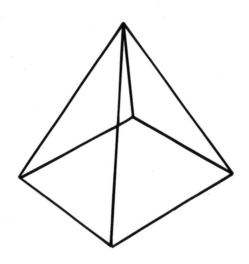

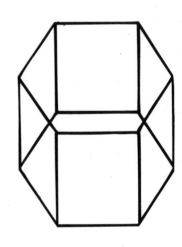

_____   _____

Complete the table below:

Name of shape	Number of faces	Number of vertices (corners)	Number of edges

Can you see a common link between the number of faces and
vertices and the number of edges? What is it?

Teachers' notes, page 142

Name

Date

Describe the shapes

Demonstrates that the child can describe 2D and 3D shapes.

Using and applying
• *Uses a range of geometrical terms.*

Ask the child to use 'shape' language to describe each shape, either orally (with you scribing) or in written form.

Note whether the child correctly uses the terms:
❏ corners or vertices
❏ sides
❏ surfaces
❏ straight
❏ right angle
❏ regular
❏ irregular

Note whether the child:
❏ uses shape names correctly

Teacher comments

Teachers' notes, page 142

Name   *Date*

Draw the shape

Demonstrates that the child can visualise shapes from descriptions.

Using and applying
• *Uses the information given.*
• *Responds to geometrical language.*

Read out, or ask the child to read, the description of each shape. Point out which shapes are 2D and which are 3. The child should write the name of the shape and draw it in the space provided.

Note whether the child understands the term:
❑ surface
❑ side
❑ corner
❑ straight
❑ curved
❑ right angle

Teacher comments

This shape has 3 corners. It has 3 straight sides. One of the corners is a right angle.

2D

This shape is regular. All the sides are the same length. There are 6 sides and 6 corners.

2D

This shape has 6 surfaces. They are all squares. There are 24 right angles on this shape.

3D

This shape rolls in a straight line. It has 3 surfaces. Two surfaces are circles, one is a rectangle that has been curved round.

3D

Teachers' notes, page 142

Name

Date

Mirror symmetry

Cut the six squares from the bottom of the page and separate them. Use these squares to make 2D shapes which have line symmetry. Use all six squares each time, and make sure that the edges line up fully with one another.

Draw the shapes you make below, and add a mirror line to each one.

For example:

How many have you found?_____

Do you think you have found them all?_____

Demonstrates the child's ability to create shapes which have line symmetry.

Using and applying
• *Uses the materials provided.*
• *Works systematically.*

Emphasise the need to use all the pieces, edge to edge, each time. While the child is working, discuss how he/she demonstrates a shape to be symmetrical. If necessary, or requested, provide a small hand-mirror.

Note whether the child:
❑ uses a mirror
❑ explains symmetry
❑ works independently

Teacher comments

Teachers' notes, page 142

✂ – – – – – – – – – –

Name

Date

Lines of symmetry

Demonstrates that the child can identify and draw lines of symmetry.

Demonstrates that the child can design shapes with line symmetry.

Using and applying
• *Uses a mirror to test for line symmetry.*

Provide a suitable hand-mirror for this task. Ask the child to draw the lines of symmetry on each pattern, using the mirror to check. Ask the child to design her/his own patterns in the empty squares, using the lines of symmetry provided.

Note whether the child can:
❑ use a mirror to find lines of reflective symmetry
❑ design symmetrical patterns

Teacher comments

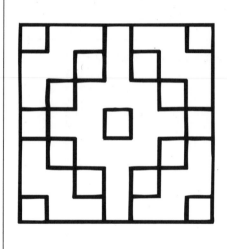

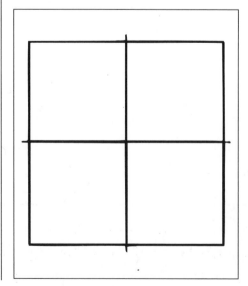

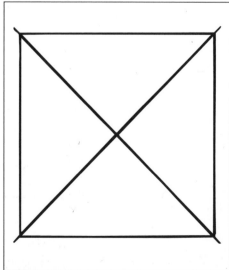

Teachers' notes, page 143

Name _____   Date _____

Rotational symmetry

Tick the shapes which have rotational symmetry.

Demonstrates the child's ability to identify rotational symmetry.

Using and applying
• *Recognises examples of rotational symmetry.*
• *Uses the materials provided.*
• *Finds ways to overcome difficulties.*

Tell the child to use other materials if these will help (see Teachers' notes). Ask the child what qualifies a shape as having rotational symmetry. The instruction at the foot of the sheet offers an extension to the task, but could be removed before copying.

Note whether the child:
❑ explains rotational symmetry
❑ understands order of rotation

Materials used (if any):

Teacher comments

Of the shapes ticked, write the order of rotation alongside each one.

Teachers' notes, page 143

Name _____ Date _____

Angle 1

Demonstrates the child's
ability to estimate and
measure angles.

Using and applying
• *Makes sensible
estimates.*
• *Uses measuring
instrument correctly.*

Provide a protractor or
angle measurer for this
activity. Encourage
estimation, and stress that
an aim of this task is to
improve ability to judge
angles. Confirm (through
discussion) that the child
knows the distinction
between an acute and an
obtuse angle, and can
describe a right angle as
being equal to a quarter-
turn. Extend the
assessment by asking
about 'reflex' angles.

*Note whether the child
can:*
❑ define a right angle
❑ define an acute angle
❑ define an obtuse angle
❑ make sensible
estimates
❑ correctly use an angle
measurer/protractor

Teacher comments

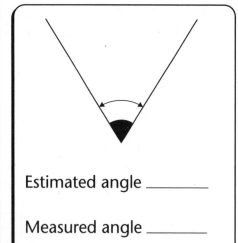

Estimated angle _____

Measured angle _____

Difference _____

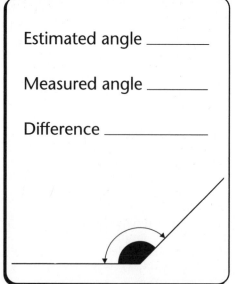

Estimated angle _____

Measured angle _____

Difference _____

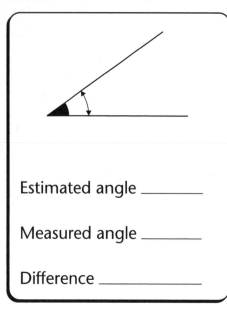

Estimated angle _____

Measured angle _____

Difference _____

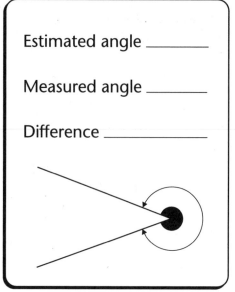

Estimated angle _____

Measured angle _____

Difference _____

Draw and measure some angles of your own:

An **acute** angle	An **obtuse** angle
Estimated angle _____	Estimated angle _____
Measured angle _____	Measured angle _____
Difference _____	Difference _____

Teachers' notes, page 143

Angle 2

Demonstrates the child's ability to calculate the external angle of a regular polygon.

Using and applying
• *Uses appropriate computer hardware and software.*
• *Selects the appropriate method and mathematics.*
• *Generalises a rule for any regular polygon.*

In this task, the angles must be found **without** simply using an angle measurer or protractor. If the child arrives at a satisfactory solution using a computer or pencil and paper method, discuss further to ascertain whether he/she can formulate a general rule for any regular polygon.

Note whether the child used:
❑ computer
❑ programmable vehicle
❑ pencil and paper method

Note also whether the child:
❑ identifies a general rule for any regular polygon

Teacher comments

Use a computer program (such as Logo), a programmable vehicle with an angle facility or a pencil and paper method to calculate the **external angles** of the regular shapes below. Do **not** measure these angles directly.

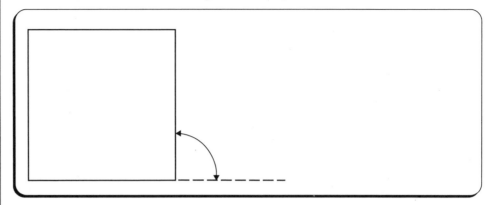

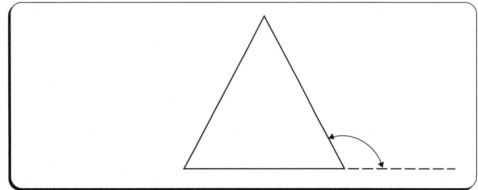

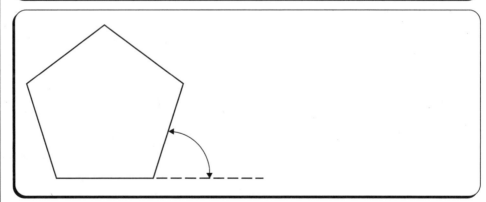

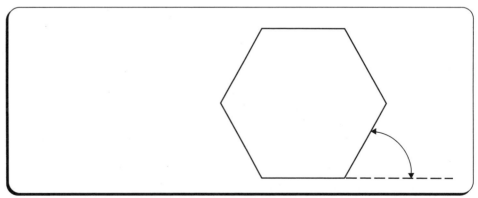

On the back of this sheet, investigate the size of the external angle of a regular octagon.

Name   *Date*

Angle 3

Demonstrates the child's ability to identify relationships between regular shapes in terms of their external and internal angles.

Using and applying
• *Shows ability to generalise.*
• *Recognises patterns.*
• *Uses tabular form of presentation.*

The child should use the ideas about internal and external angles explored in 'Angle 2'. He/she should be encouraged to select equipment for this task. Talk through the child's written responses. Retain other pieces of written or pictorial evidence, such as calculations or drawings used in working out.

Note whether the child:
❏ works independently of others
❏ works without teacher support

Specific materials or methods used:

Teacher comments

Fill in this table.

	Equilateral triangle	Square	Regular pentagon	Regular hexagon
Internal angle				
No. of sides				
Sum of internal angles				
External angle				
No. of external angles				
Sum of external angles				

What do you notice about your answers in the two shaded rows?

Calculate the sum of the internal angles and the sum of the external angles for a regular shape of your choice.

Teachers' notes, page 144

Name

Date

Nets of shapes

Using squares from a construction kit, find different nets for a cube. Draw them below. One has been done for you.

Demonstrates the child's ability to model and visualise nets for cubes.

Using and applying
- *Finds several solutions.*
- *Uses trial and improvement.*
- *Records pictorially.*

Provide suitable construction materials. Encourage the child to create cube shapes and then 'unpick' them in various ways. Observe how the child finds different nets.

Note whether the child can:
❑ work independently
❑ work methodically

Teacher comments

How many have you found?

Have you found them all?

Teachers' notes, page 144

Name

Date

Area and perimeter

What are the maximum and minimum perimeters possible when you arrange 4 squares edge to edge? Draw the different arrangements below. One has been done for you.

Demonstrates the child's ability to investigate relationships between area and perimeter.

Using and applying
• *Works methodically.*
• *Observes patterns.*
• *Draws conclusions.*
• *Tabulates results (optional).*

Provide squared paper if requested. Talk to the child about the work he/she is doing, and establish whether any general rules are emerging. Tabulation of the results for different numbers of squares is an appropriate extension of this task.

Note whether the child:
❏ identifies the minimum and maximum perimeters correctly
❏ identifies a pattern
Pattern identified:

Teacher comments

perimeter = 10 units

Now try using a different number of squares. Continue on the back of the sheet if you need more space.

You may want to make a table of your results for different numbers of squares. Is there a pattern?

Name

Date

Same area, different shape

This trapezium has an area of 12 square units.

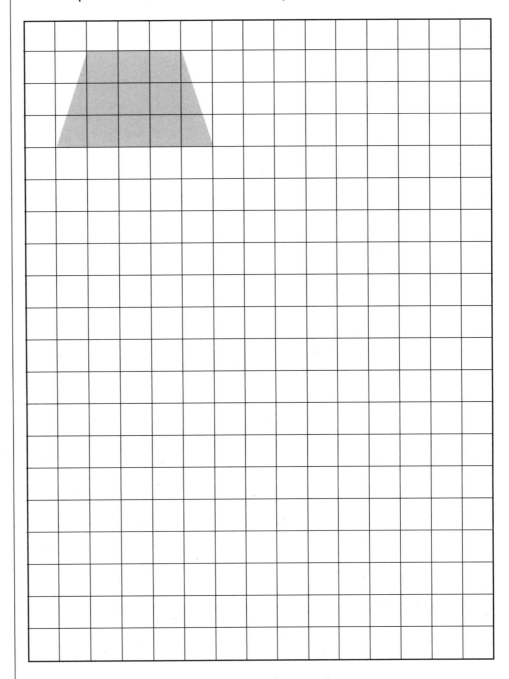

Demonstrates the child's ability to calculate area by adding whole and part squares.

Using and applying
• Finds ways of overcoming difficulties.
• Uses trial and improvement.
• Explains methods used.

Draw the child's attention to the trapezium, but do not explain how you know that the area is 12 square units. Stress the need for a pencil sketching to allow amendment of unsuccessful attempts.

Note whether the child:
❏ uses trial and improvement
❏ works independently of others
❏ works without teacher support

Teacher comments

Use a pencil to draw and shade in a triangle, a rectangle, a hexagon and a pentagon. Each shape must have an area of **12 square units**. The shapes do not need to be regular.

You will need to work by trial and improvement. Use more squared paper if necessary.

Name

Date

Enlargement

Draw a triangle on the grid using the following co-ordinates: (2,1), (1,3), (4,4).

Demonstrates the child's ability to enlarge a shape by a scale of factor 2 or 3, and to link this to the increase in area.

Using and applying
• *Records work graphically.*
• *Follows instructions.*
• *Identifies relationship between scale factor enlargement and area.*

Explain to the child that the activity sheet is in 3 sections. Observe how the child works through each of these. In particular, note how the child compares the areas of the triangles. Talk to the child about predicting the area under scale factor 4 enlargement.

Note whether the child:
❑ uses co-ordinates correctly
❑ calculates ratio of areas
❑ identifies link between areas for scale factor 2 and 3
❑ works independently

Teacher comments

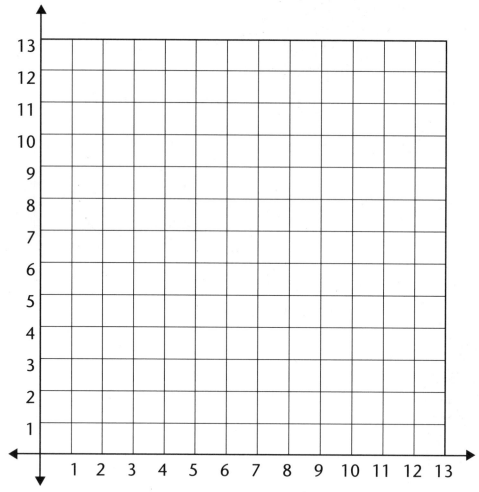

Double each of the co-ordinates to give a new set of points.

Is the new triangle **similar** to the first one? _____

How many times bigger is the area of the larger triangle?

_____

What happens if you triple the co-ordinates? Draw the shape on the graph and comment on the result here.

Teachers' notes, page 145

SCHOLASTIC
Portfolio
ASSESSMENT

MEASURING

MEASURES

The activities in this chapter cover several types of measure – length, area, volume, capacity, mass and time. They offer a balance of skills-based and investigational tasks.

Prior knowledge and experience

The child will have experienced certain basic aspects of measurement before Key Stage 2 (Primary 4–7):
• early language of measurement and comparison;
• measuring with non-standard units, leading to an awareness of the need for standard units;
• measuring with a variety of standard units linked to the scale of the items being measured;
• measuring with a variety of equipment.

Progression through Key Stage 2

An important feature of maths work at this stage is the extension of standard units of measure above and below the 'convenient' units already encountered. In doing this, it is important to recognise the interrelatedness of units within our metric (Base 10) system (for example, 1km = 1000m, 1m = 100cm, 1cm = 10mm.

This interrelatedness extends between different kinds of metric measure. A millilitre of water, for example, occupies a volume of 1 cubic centimetre, which in turn has a mass of 1g. This is quite a complex concept to grasp, and will need revisiting as the child moves towards the end of Key Stage 2. It will provide a basis for understanding such concepts as density in later work.

METRIC AND IMPERIAL MEASURES

Although there has been a concerted move towards metrication in Britain over the past few decades, there remains a widespread usage of imperial measures which we continue to encounter in our everyday lives. Consequently, we need to ensure that the child has a working knowledge of the commonly used imperial units and an idea of their scale relative to comparable metric measures.

Conventions of recording

In all cases except time, the recording of measurement is closely allied to the decimal system. The child will need to develop a clear sense of place value if he/she is going to be adequately prepared to convert from one unit of measure to another. For example, converting 1060m to 1.06km requires a specific awareness of zero as a place holder: the first zero is retained under conversion to hold the place value of the 6 digit; but the second zero has no significance under conversion and is thus dropped.

You will need to talk to the child to ensure that the appropriate convention is used when reading back a written measure. For example, 3.32kg is '3 point three two kilograms', *not* '3 point thirty-two kilograms'. However the same convention does not apply to time: 3.32pm is 'three thirty-two pm', *not* 'three point three two pm'.

METHODS AND RESOURCES

The use of formulae

While the most able child will be able to learn and apply formulae to calculate the areas and volumes of regular shapes, this is not a principal objective for the majority of pupils in England and Wales. This is not to say, however, that the average child cannot work with basic 'short-cut' methods, such as calculating the area of a rectangle by multiplying the length by the width. Use of formulae is stipulated by the Scottish Guidelines for

Mathematics (at Level E) and by the Northern Ireland Curriculum for Mathematics at Key Stage 2.

The use of equipment

As the child becomes more competent in the different kinds of measurement, he/she should be made aware of the potential choice of equipment. If the equipment to be used is always given directly to the child, he/she will have no opportunity to demonstrate the knowledge that (for example) length is measured by certain pieces of equipment and not others. Within a given type of measurement, the child will also need to be able to choose the most appropriate piece of equipment (such as a ruler, a tape measure or a trundle wheel). By encouraging the child to choose from a range of instruments rather than specifying one, the teacher will be able to make a fuller assessment of the child's response to some of the more challenging tasks.

TEACHING NOTES FOR INDIVIDUAL ACTIVITIES

How do you measure it?
page 174

Knowledge and use of measuring equipment You will need to decide whether to make the relevant measuring equipment available to the child when he/she is engaged in this task. In the most difficult version of the task, the child can be asked to draw the instruments from memory. Typical solutions are: 1. height measure stick 2. measuring jug 3. trundle wheel 4. kitchen scales 5. bathroom scales 6. stopwatch.

A child with extensive experience of using a wide range of measuring equipment will be able to complete this task from memory. A younger or less experienced child will need to select appropriate items from a collection of equipment, and even then may not always choose the most appropriate item (for example, he/she may suggest a tape measure for measuring height).

Length
How long are your
leaves?
page 175

Estimating and measuring with a ruler Before this task, you should collect a tray of leaves of various sorts and sizes. If you plan to spread the activity over several sessions, you will need to keep replenishing the tray as the leaves become floppy and torn through handling.

This task will allow you to assess the child's ability to estimate. Most children will be able to make reasonable estimates of leaf size by the end of the task, even if their first few estimates are wildly inaccurate. Some children at an earlier stage may measure to the nearest cm; most should be able to measure to the nearest 0.5cm; some more confident or older children may measure to the nearest mm. The child's choice will indicate her/his competence in reading measurements from a scale.

Measuring around
page 176

Estimating and measuring using a tape measure Before this task, you should collect a group of 15 objects with curved surfaces that the child can measure around, such as containers, cups, plates, saucers, tins and balls. Give each object a number for easy reference when measuring, so that the child does not have to name and distinguish each object.

The child's estimates of circumference should improve during the task. He/she may become aware that the circumference of a round object is just over three times its diameter (see 'Circles', page 170). The measurements should be recorded to the nearest centimetre (cm), 0.5 centimetre or millimetre (mm), depending on the child's level of competence in reading a measuring scale.

The relationship between the diameter and the circumference of a circle This task can be undertaken by children regardless of whether or not they have been introduced to the idea of a fixed ratio between the diameter and the circumference of a circle. As the activity involves measuring a curved edge, the child may request string or a fabric measuring tape. Alternatively, the child may roll the edge along a flat surface to provide a straight-line measure.

The ratio between the circumference and diameter of a circle is constant, regardless of the size of the circle. This ratio is known as pi (π) and is approximately 3.14 (close to, but not equal to, 22/7). An able child may already be aware of the ratio between the circumference and diameter. Such a child will confirm this knowledge when he/she discusses the work. If not, he/she may recognise the fact that the circumference is always '3 and a bit' times the diameter. The observed ratio will vary due to the approximate nature of measurement.

Even though many children may not recognise the relationship, some may still work through the task with a high degree of independence. Such children will select appropriate measuring instruments for themselves and record the results with due care and accuracy. The younger or less able child will need support in using the equipment and recording the results.

Using length measurements to create a scale drawing Decide how open the task will be, in terms of both what is drawn and the selection of a suitable scale. As this assessment is wide-ranging, you should give the minimum amount of support necessary to provide access.

A confident child will select a scale for him/herself based on the size of the object and the size of the grid. Equipment should be selected in relation to the size of the object; a playground, for example, might be measured using a long (10m) tape measure or trundle wheel. A less experienced child may need to be directed to a suitable object for measuring, and may find it difficult to choose a scale. Such a child may also use estimation for some of the drawing, rather than taking a measurement for each construction line.

If necessary, discuss the idea of correspondence with the child – for example, on a scale of 1:10 000, 5cm on the grid corresponds to 500m in reality.

Investigating surface areas of simple shapes The child needs to understand that the 'exposed' surface area in this task means the visible area (not in contact with the table). The possible solutions for three cubes are as shown in Figure 1.

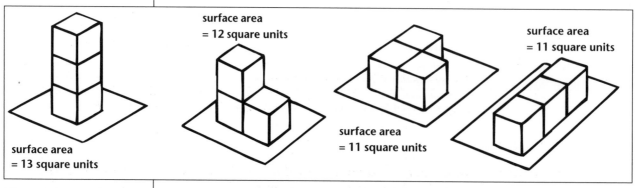

surface area = 13 square units

surface area = 12 square units

surface area = 11 square units

surface area = 11 square units

Figure 1

An able child will find the four solutions and may note that the maximum visible surface area is achieved, regardless of the number of cubes, when the arrangement is a single upright tower of cubes – that is, a shape with as little of its surface as possible in contact with the table. A younger or less able child may not find all the solutions, and may count two orientations of the same arrangement as 'different'.

Volume and surface area
page 180

Varying the surface area for a constant volume You will need sufficient interlocking cubes to allow 24 per child (or 36 if the extension task is to be undertaken). There are 6 possible solutions for the main task (see Figure 2), given that the dimensions are limited to whole numbers.

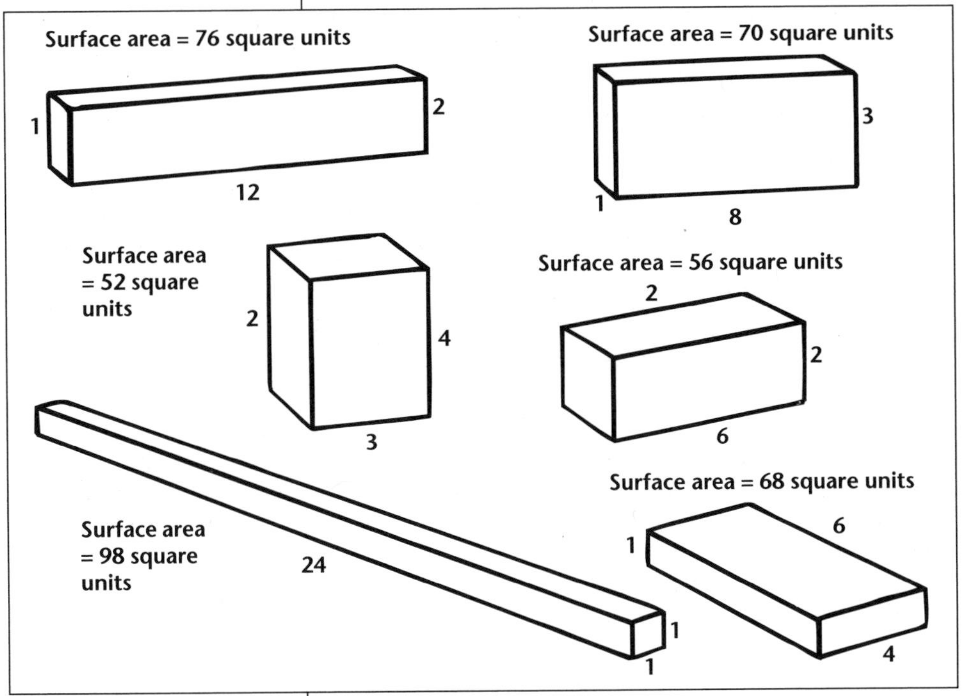

A child with experience in work of this type, and a systematic approach, may find all the possible solutions by using knowledge of the factors of 24. Such a child may also disregard the interlocking cubes and produce outline drawings alone. The surface area will be accurately calculated by working out the total area of the three pairs of faces, the child may realise that for a cuboid,

Surface area = 76 square units

Surface area = 70 square units

Surface area = 52 square units

Surface area = 56 square units

Surface area = 98 square units

Surface area = 68 square units

Figure 2

opposite faces are identical. Exceptionally, a child may note that the 4 × 3 × 2 cuboid (which most closely approximates to a cube) has the smallest surface area, whereas the most 'stretched' cuboid has the greatest surface area.

A less able child will make all the shapes and count all the squares on each face to find the surface area. It is likely that a younger child will need some support in sketching the cuboid and in finding the surface area.

Volume and capacity
How much is in the jug?
page 181

Reading from and marking on a scale The child should be able to complete the first part of the task quickly and independently, confirming that he/she can identify 50ml graduations in between marked hundreds. If the child works inaccurately or struggles with this, you may wish to postpone the second part of the task until a later date. If this happens, date the first and second parts to indicate the interval between them.

The second part of the task requires the child to use finer (marked) graduations of 10ml between labelled hundreds. Again, a child at the beginning of Key Stage 2 should be able to apply her/his ability to count in tens to this task.

What order?
page 182

Ordering containers based on their capacity This task could be simplified by removing the requirement to measure (with a standard), so that the child only needs to make comparative operations. Alternatively, the number of containers to be ordered could be reduced.

A water tray or plastic storage container will be needed. Adding a proprietary water colourant before the activity will also help with reading the water levels. A plank of wood across the tray will provide a useful platform for ordering the containers. (See Figure 3).

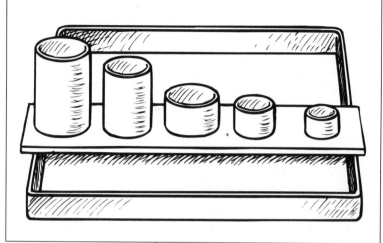

Figure 3

Observe the child's practical work closely, as this forms the basis of the assessment. The containers can be ordered by several different methods and no single method is necessarily more indicative of ability. The child might:
- use a capacity measure to gauge the amount of water in each container;
- use an ungraduated container and mark the water levels achieved by each of the containers with a marker pen;
- pour from one container to another to compare the capacities directly. The more able child will complete the task in its intended form – that is, by reading from a scale on a capacity measure. A younger child may need to work with direct comparison, finding the order but not the capacity values.

Mass
Weighing out the potatoes
page 183

Estimating mass, reading from a dial accurately You will need a bag of potatoes for the children to use. The child's estimates may initially be wildly inaccurate, but they should become more reasonable as the task goes on. A child at the beginning of Key Stage 2 should be able to read from the dial accurately and record in g. Asking the child to mark the dials with the heaviest and lightest potatoes gives you the opportunity to check her/his use of the scales.

Comparing measures
Is it true?
page 184

Knowledge of units within and between different measures This task assumes a high level of prior knowledge, specifically regarding the Base 10 nature of metric measure. The solutions are as follows: 1. true 2. true 3. true 4. true 5. true 6. false 7. false 8. false.

By the end of Key Stage 2, most children should be flexible in moving from one unit to another, provided that they have had opportunities to make these important connections. A child who is successful in sorting all the statements correctly is likely to be at this stage. A correct sorting of statements 1 and 2, backed up by verbal explanation, will indicate readiness to deal with the concept of density.

Which is greater?
page 185

Knowledge/comparison of metric and imperial measures Before attempting this task, the child should have worked with both metric and imperial measures and have developed a general appreciation of their relative magnitude. The solutions are: 1 litre is greater than 1 pint; 1 mile is greater than 1 kilometre; 1 kilogram is greater than 1 pound; 1 inch is greater than 1 centimetre; 1 metre is greater than 1 yard; 1 gallon is greater than 1 litre.

A child who is aware of metric and imperial measures may be able to sort the labels into the two groups and, within each group, to identify the type of measure to which each refers (such as length or mass). Only the most able child, however, is likely to be able to identify the pairs correctly and to say which of each pair is the greater. Many children will tend to form

MEASURING

statements which are true but which involve inappropriate comparisons, such as '1 metre is greater than 1 inch'.

Time
Catching the bus
page 186

Calculating times in five-minute intervals The partial information given in the timetables should allow the child to work out the missing times; the second timetable is more difficult than the first. A child who can tell the time competently at five-minute intervals should be able to complete both timetables accurately. A key aspect of this task is the ability to count to 60 in fives. Children who identify and use this fact will work more quickly and confidently.

Catching the train
page 187

Using the 24-hour clock After the child has completed the first part of the sheet, you should check her/his answers to make sure that she/he has the necessary information to go on to the second part. (The answers are: 40 minutes; 25 minutes; 20 minutes; 50 minutes; 2 hours and 15 minutes; day.) When working on the second (incomplete) timetable, a child who is confident will be able to work out the times both by working forwards and by working back, and will record accurately using the 24-hour notation in digital form. Asking the child to note whether the arrival time is

London Euston	14.30	21.40	11.10
Milton Keynes	15.10	22.20	11.50
Northampton	15.35	22.45	12.15
Rugby	15.55	23.05	12.35
Birmingham New Street	16.45	23.55	13.25
	day	night	day

Figure 4

during the day or night will help to indicate her/his ability to connect the 24-hour clock with real experience. The completed second timetable is shown in Figure 4.

Time to investigate
page 188

Recalling, understanding and using units of time This activity can be carried out using pencil and paper alone, drawing on the child's recall of the units of time. However, the child may need support with some parts of the task, and thus it may be appropriate to provide items such as a calculator and a calendar.

Assessment of this activity should have two principal foci: the extent to which the child works without additional resources; and the depth of understanding shown in the answers. A child whose knowledge of time measurement is still developing may need to use a calendar or diary to establish the number of days in each month. He/she may have a vague or incomplete understanding of leap years – for example, saying 'They come every four years' (but not which years) or 'Leap years have a different number of days' (but not what the difference is).

An older or more able child may already know the number of days in each month and be able to give more detail about leap years – for example, saying that a leap year is 366 days (one more than usual), that the extra day is February 29th or that the leap years are those that divide exactly by 4. He/she may be able to explain that every fourth year is counted as a leap year in order to compensate for the fact that the Earth's orbit around the Sun takes approximately 365¼ days.

In the final investigation, a child working at a more basic level may answer only the first question (calculating in days) and take no account of leap years. A child working more thoroughly may be able to calculate in minutes and seconds, and may take account of leap years in order to answer more accurately. The child may need a calculator to complete this task.

Name   *Date*

Demonstrates the child's
knowledge of a range of
measuring instruments
and their use.

Using and applying
• *Selects appropriate
materials.*
• *Understands and uses
the language of
measures.*

This activity might be
carried out by the child
working unaided and
without access to
measuring equipment.
Stress that there may
sometimes be more than
one satisfactory solution,
but that the choice made
must be appropriate for
the task.

Note whether the child:
❑ works without support
makes appropriate
selections for
❑ mass
❑ time
❑ length/height
❑ capacity/volume

Teacher comments

How do you measure it?

Draw and name the instruments you might use to measure
the following:

1. The height of your friend

2. Rain collected in a cup

3. The perimeter of the
school grounds

4. The mass of a bowlful of
sugar

5. The mass of your friend

6. The time in seconds
taken to run 60m

Teachers' notes, page 169

Name

Date

How long are your leaves?

Demonstrates that the child can make sensible estimates of length, measure it to the nearest 0.5cm and record measurements.

Using and applying
• *Uses a ruler appropriately.*
• *Modifies and improves estimates over the course of the task.*

Provide a collection of different-sized leaves. Ask the child to estimate and then measure the length of 20 different leaves to the nearest 0.5cm, recording the results as he/she goes along. Remind the child to try to make close estimates, and to look for and explain any change in her/his estimating by the end of the task.

Note whether the child can:
❑ measure accurately with a ruler
❑ record measurements of length
❑ estimate sensibly

Teacher comments

	My estimate	My measurement
1		
2		
3		
4		
5		
6		
7		
8		
9		
10		
11		
12		
13		
14		
15		
16		
17		
18		
19		
20		

Teachers' notes, page 169

Tick where your estimate and your measurement are only 1cm or less apart.

How many ticks? _____

What did you notice about your estimates by the end of the task?

_____

_____

_____

_____

My longest leaf

_____

My shortest leaf

_____

The difference between the longest and the shortest leaf

_____

_____

Name

Date

Measuring around

Demonstrates that the child can make sensible estimates of circumference, measure it to the nearest 0.5cm and record measurements.

Using and applying
• Uses a tape measure accurately.
• Modifies and improves estimates over the course of the task.

Provide a collection of 15 numbered objects (see Teachers' notes). Ask the child to estimate and then measure around each object to the nearest 0.5cm, recording as he/she goes along. Remind the child to try to make close estimates, and to look for and explain any change in her/his estimating by the end of the task.

Note whether the child can:
❏ measure the circumference of curved objects accurately
❏ use a tape measure accurately
❏ record using 0.5cm intervals

Teacher comments

My estimate	My measurement
1	
2	
3	
4	
5	
6	
7	
8	
9	
10	
11	
12	
13	
14	
15	

Tick where your estimate and your measurement are only 1cm or less apart.

How many ticks? _____

What did you notice about your estimates by the end of the task?

_____

_____

_____

_____

_____

Did you do anything to help you get better at estimating?

_____

_____

_____

_____

_____

Teachers' notes, page 169

Circles

Demonstrates the child's ability to measure the circumference of a circle.

Demonstrates the child's awareness of the relationship between the circumference and the diameter of a circle.

Using and applying
* *Searches for a pattern.*
* *Makes general statements.*
* *Selects materials for a task.*

Do not specify what measuring equipment or calculation methods might be used. Encourage the child to look in detail at the results to find a general relationship. Establish whether the child has any prior awareness of this relationship.

Note whether the child:
❑ identifies the relationship
❑ already knows the relationship
❑ can name the constant pi (π)

Materials used:

Teacher comments

Measure the circumference and diameter of a range of objects with circular edges or faces (for example, the top edge of a round paper bin). Find both large and small circles to measure. Record your results in the table below.

object	circumference	diameter

What do you notice about the relationship between the circumference and the diameter?

_____

_____

_____

_____

_____

_____

Name   *Date*

Demonstrates the child's ability to use length measurements to create a scale drawing.

Using and applying
• *Selects appropriate mathematics.*
• *Selects appropriate materials.*
• *Develops own strategies.*

Either give a free choice or specify the subject of the drawing. Make sure the child understands that a scale drawing must be based on accurate measurements. Explain that it is important to select a scale such that the drawing fits the grid provided. Encourage the selection of any suitable measuring instruments and aids to calculation.

Note whether the child:
❑ uses a scale consistently
❑ selects an appropriate scale without assistance

Materials used:

Teacher comments

Scale drawing

Use a suitable scale to create a drawing of your desk, the classroom, the playground or someone in your class.

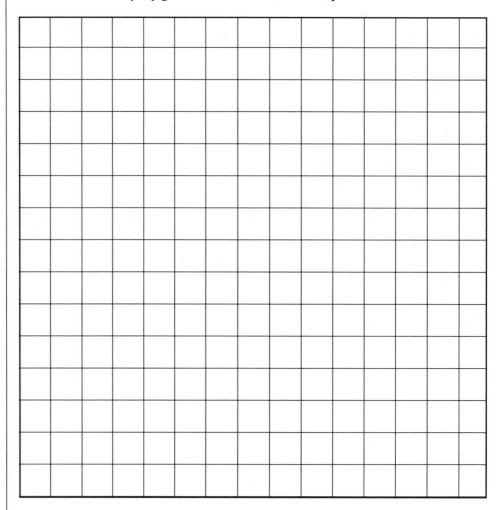

This is a scale drawing of _____

The scale of my drawing is:

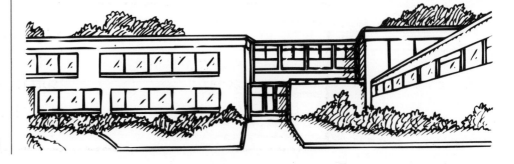

Teachers' notes, page 170

Name

Date

Surface area

Two cubes can be connected together and placed on the table in two different ways:

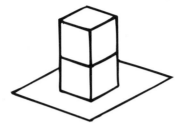

The number of exposed faces is 9.

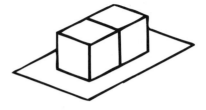

The number of exposed faces is 8.

Investigate the number of exposed faces (surface area) if three cubes are connected together and placed on the table. Draw the possible arrangements. Write the surface area alongside each one.

Have you found them all?

What is the maximum surface area?

☐ square units

What is the minimum surface area?

☐ square units

Demonstrates the child's ability to investigate the surface area of simple structures.

Using and applying
• Constructs or visualises arrangements.
• Presents results clearly.
• Uses diagrams.

Provide three interlocking cubes for each child. As an option, you could provide isometric paper, though some children will find this more problematic than freehand drawing. Make sure the child understands what is meant by 'exposed' and 'surface area' in this activity.

Note whether the child:
❑ calculates surface area accurately (by counting)
❑ identifies maximum and minimum surface area
❑ finds all possible arrangements

Teacher comments

Teachers' notes, page 170

Volume and surface area

Make and draw four different cuboids with a volume of 24 unit cubes each. For each one, calculate the total surface area (including the bottom of the shape).

Demonstrates the child's ability to investigate shapes of different surface area for a given constant volume.

Using and applying
• *Represents work using diagrams.*
• *Works systematically.*

Provide interlocking cubes for this task. Discuss how the solutions are found, and assess the use of relevant vocabulary. Encourage the child to use the back of the sheet for the extension task.

Note whether the child:
❑ calculates surface area correctly
❑ is aware of the formula for calculating the volume of a cuboid

Teacher comments

Volume = 24 unit cubes

Surface area = _____

Volume = 24 unit cubes

Surface area = _____

Volume = 24 unit cubes

Surface area = _____

Volume = 24 unit cubes

Surface area = _____

Now investigate for cuboids made from 36 unit cubes.

Teachers' notes, page 171

Name   *Date*

How much is in the jug?

Teachers' notes, page 171

Demonstrates that the child can read the scale on a measuring jug.

Demonstrates that the child can mark a given amount of liquid on a scale.

Using and applying
• *Uses a scale accurately.*

Ask the child to complete the sheet by reading the scale and writing down the amount of liquid in ml, or by marking the stated amount of liquid on the scale.

Note whether the child can:
❑ read a scale to the nearest 50 ml
❑ read a scale to the nearest 10 ml
❑ mark on a scale to 50ml
❑ mark on a scale to 10ml

Teacher comments

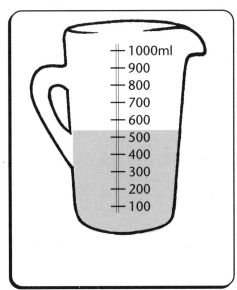

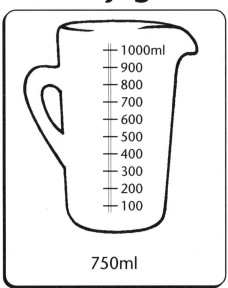

750ml

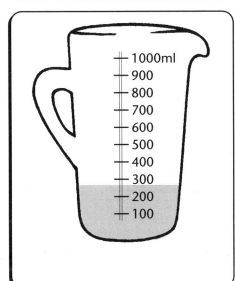

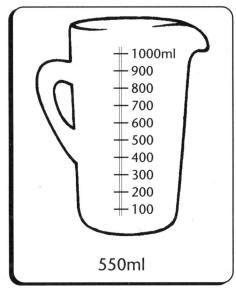

550ml

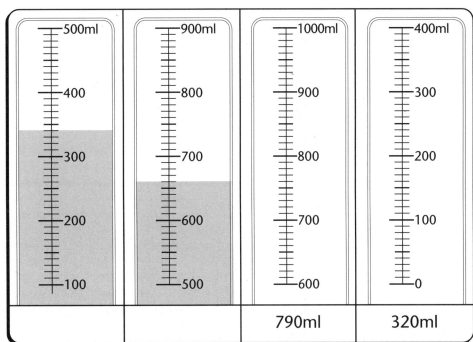

790ml   320ml

Name

Date

What order?

You need some bottles and/or small containers. Find out how much water each one holds. Put them in order, starting with the lowest capacity.

Demonstrates the child's ability to order a set of containers based on their capacities.

Using and applying
• Selects appropriate materials.
• Takes increasing responsibility for tasks.

Provide five suitable containers. Introduce the activity without specifying the additional equipment required. Encourage the child to write or draw a review of how the activity was carried out. Observe the range of measuring equipment used, and the appropriateness of its use.

Note whether the child:
❑ works unaided
❑ measures with appropriate accuracy

Equipment used:

Teacher comments

Teachers' notes, page 171

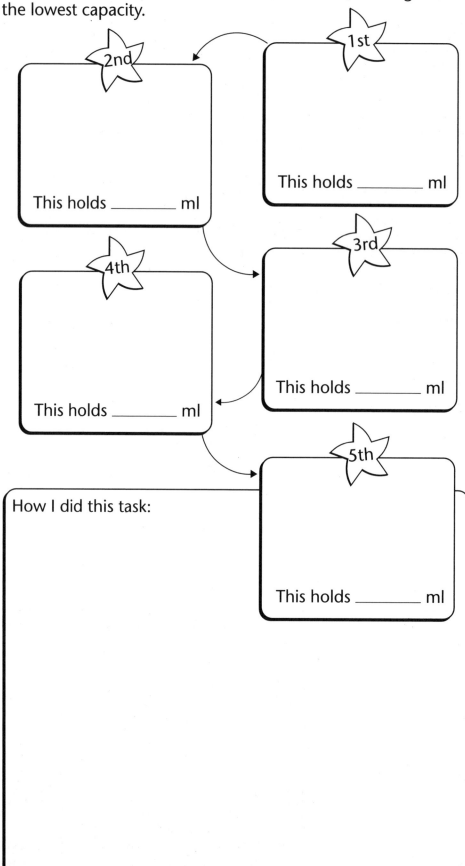

2nd

This holds _____ ml

1st

This holds _____ ml

4th

This holds _____ ml

3rd

This holds _____ ml

5th

This holds _____ ml

How I did this task:

Name

Date

Weighing out the potatoes

Demonstrates that the child can measure mass in kg and g.

Using and applying
• *Estimates and measures.*
• *Reads from a dial.*
• *Records with accuracy.*

Ask the child to weigh a selection of potatoes one by one. As the child goes along, he/she should record an estimate for each potato and then the correct measurement. Then ask the child to write down and mark on the dials the masses of the heaviest and lightest potatoes.

Note whether the child can:
❑ read from a dial accurately
❑ mark on a dial accurately
❑ make sensible estimates
❑ record accurately

Teacher comments

	My estimate	My measurement
1		
2		
3		
4		
5		
6		
7		
8		
9		
10		

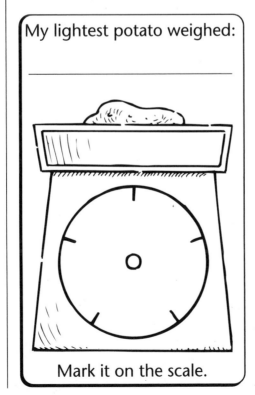

My lightest potato weighed:

_____

Mark it on the scale.

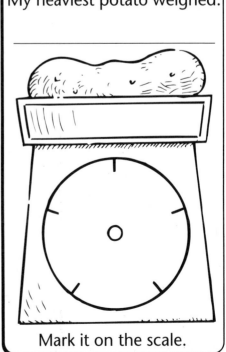

My heaviest potato weighed:

_____

Mark it on the scale.

Teachers' notes, page 172

Name

Date

Is it true?

True	False

Demonstrates the child's knowledge of equivalent units within measures.

Demonstrates the child's understanding of the relationships between different measures.

Using and applying
• **Selects appropriate mathematics.**
• **Develops strategies to solve problems.**

Explain that the statements at the bottom of the sheet describe relationships between different units of measurement. Some relate to one kind of measurement, others to more than one kind (for example, volume and mass).
Ask the child to cut out each statement and stick it into one of the columns, depending on whether he/she thinks it is true or false. Discuss the child's answers to draw out her/his understanding of the physical principles involved.

Note whether the child demonstrates a sound grasp of problems involving:
❑ mass
❑ capacity
❑ volume
❑ length

Teacher comments

1. A litre of water has a mass of one kilogram.

2. A litre of water will fit into a container with internal dimensions of 10cm × 10cm × 10cm.

3. A centilitre is equal to 10 millilitres.

4. There are one million millimetres in a kilometre.

5. A millilitre of water has a volume of one cubic centimetre.

6. There are 100 metres in a kilometre.

7. A kilogram of metal weighs more than a kilogram of wood.

8. Volume can be measured in centimetres.

Teachers' notes, page 172

Name

Date

Which is greater?

Demonstrates the child's knowledge of, and ability to, compare metric and imperial measures.

Using and applying
• **Checks results.**
• **Talks about the work.**
• **Explains reasoning.**

Tell the child to cut out the labels at the bottom of the page and place them in the appropriate spaces to compare imperial with metric units. Explain the need to match related measures (for example, of length or of mass) together. When the child has filled all the spaces and checked that the statements make sense and are correct, he/ she should stick the labels in place.

Note whether the child
❏ can distinguish imperial from metric measures
finds the correct solutions for
❏ length
❏ mass
❏ capacity

Teacher comments

is greater than

is greater than

is greater than

is greater than

is greater than

is greater than

Teachers' notes, page 172

✂ - - - - - - - - - - -

1 mile	1 inch	1 yard	1 pound
1 kilogram	1 gallon	1 kilometre	1 litre
1 metre	1 litre	1 pint	1 centimetre

Demonstrates that the child can read the time in digital form.

Demonstrates that the child can calculate times in steps of 5 minutes.

Using and applying
• Solves problems involving measures of time.
• Devises own methods of using information to calculate further facts.

Ask the child to fill in the empty parts of the bus timetable using the information provided. Then ask the child to use the map and timetable to answer the questions at the foot of the sheet. He/she should give the shortest times possible (that is, travelling directly).

Note whether the child can:
❏ record time in 5-minute intervals
❏ use the timetable correctly

Teacher comments

Catching the bus

The bus goes from Upton to the main bus station and back. It takes 20 minutes to get from one end of its route to the other. The bus stops every 5 minutes on the way, and spends 5 minutes waiting at each end.
Fill in the bus timetable below.

Bus station to Upton			
Upton	9.00	9.50	
Cinema	9.05		10.45
Park			
Railway Stn		10.05	
Bus Stn			11.00

Bus station to Upton			
Bus Stn	9.25		
Railway Stn		10.20	
Park			
Cinema	9.40		
Upton			11.25

How long does the bus take to get from Upton to the Park?

_____

How long does it take to get from the bus station to the cinema?

_____

How long does it take to get from the cinema to the bus station?

_____

Name _____ *Date* _____

Catching the train

Demonstrates that the child can interpret and write times according to the 24-hour clock.

Using and applying
* *Solves problems involving measures of time.*
* *Works methodically.*

Ask the child to use the first timetable to work out the intervals between stations and the duration of the whole journey. Then ask the child to use this information to complete the second timetable, noting whether each train reaches Birmingham New Street in the daytime or at night.

Note whether the child can:
❏ use 24-hour notation accurately
❏ calculate intervals of time

Teacher comments

London Euston	12.05
Milton Keynes	12.45
Northampton	13.10
Rugby	13.30
Birmingham New Street	14.20

How long does each part of the journey take?

1. _____

2. _____

3. _____

4. _____

How long does the journey take altogether? _____

Does this journey take place during the day or at night?

_____

Now use the journey times above to fill in the gaps in this timetable. Assume the train takes the same amount of time as above.

London Euston	14.30		
Milton Keynes			
Northampton		22.45	
Rugby			
Birmingham New Street			13.25

Do you arrive during the day or at night?   day/night   day/night   day/night

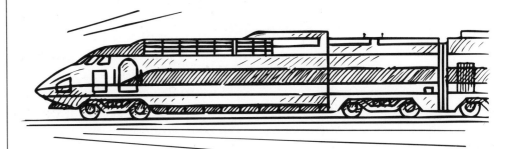

Teachers' notes, page 173

Name   *Date*

Time to investigate

Demonstrates the child's ability to recall, understand and use units of time.

Using and applying
• *Develops own strategies.*
• *Knows the conventions and units of time measurement.*
• *Applies knowledge to solve problems.*

Tell the child that the first part of the sheet assesses her/his knowledge about days, months and years and the second part requires her/him to apply this knowledge. Encourage the child to carry out the final task on the back of the sheet and to show all her/his working. Leave the method and use of materials (if any) for this task open for the child to decide.

Note whether the child:
❑ works independently
❑ knows how many days are in each month

Equipment used for final task (if any):

Teacher comments

How many days are there in each of the 12 months?

Jan _____ days	Feb _____ days	Mar _____ days
Apr _____ days	May _____ days	Jun _____ days
Jul _____ days	Aug _____ days	Sep _____ days
Oct _____ days	Nov _____ days	Dec _____ days

What do you know about leap years? Explain:

What is different about a leap year? _____

_____

_____

How many days are in a leap year? _____

When do leap years happen? _____

_____

When is the next leap year? _____

Why do we have leap years? _____

_____

_____

_____

_____

You may want to use what you have written above to help with the next investigation. Use the space overleaf to answer the question, and show all your working.

How many days have you been alive?
How many minutes (approximately)?
How many seconds (approximately)?

Teachers' notes, page 173

188

SCOTTISH 5–14 GUIDELINES FOR MATHEMATICS

In this grid, each activity is referenced to the relevant attainment outcome. Within this attainment outcome, the strand and level are identified. The strand is coded to match the level **within which** the child will be working. Please note that completion of a task does not necessarily indicate achievement at that level.

The probability activities in Chapter 2 relate to higher levels in the Scottish Guidelines.

Number, money and measurement

NUMBER	Range & type of numbers	Money	Add & subtract	Multiply & divide	Round numbers	Fractions, % and ratio	Patterns & sequences	Functions & equations	Position & movement
Number chains	C								
The morning post	B								
Quick off the grid 1	C								
Quick off the grid 2	C								
Which is closer? 1	C								
Which is closer? 2	C								
Jumping in tens			B, C						
Adding fives			B, C				C		
Spot the pattern			B, C				C		
All in order			B, C						
Addition grid			B						
Missing numbers			B, C				B, C		
Pick and mix			B, C						
Target 10			B, C				C		
Target 20			B, C				C		
Target 100 (a)			C						
Target 100 (b)			C	C					
Target 100 (c)			C						
Triple bonds			C						
Age gap			C						
In my head 1			B						
Explaining how you did it 1			C						
Taking away			C						
What's the difference? 1			C						
What's the difference? 2			C						
What's the difference? 3			C						
What's the difference? 4			C						
What's the difference? 5			C						
Countdown to zero	C								
Keep on adding			B, C						
Find the product 1				C					
Find the product 2				C, D					
Testing times! 1				C					
Testing times! 2				C					
Testing times! 3				C					
Number bugs							C, D		
Perfect bugs							C, D		
Puzzling times				C			C		
Square numbers 1							D, E		
Square numbers 2	D, E						D, E		
Cube numbers							D, E		
Keep on taking away			C	C					
Mix and match				C					
Explaining how you did it 2				C, D					
Division One				D					
Premier Division				D					
Find four facts			B, C						
Fill in the gaps			C	C					
In my head 2				C					
In my head 3				C, D					
Blank cheques 1		C, D							
Blank cheques 2		C, D							
European survey		D, E							
Below zero	D, E								
Real numbers	D								
Fractions 1						C			
Fractions 2						C, D			
Fractions 3						D			
Fractions 4						C, D			
Percentages						D			
Spot the pattern							B		
What did I do?								C	
What comes later?							D		
Spot the rule							C, D		
Double trouble						C			
Input, output 1								C, D	D
Input, output 2								D	D
Input, output 3								D	D
Trampoline party		D							
A sound deal		D							
Shopper's choice		D							
Find it!				C	C				
Round the block								D	
Nearest numbers				C					
Hundreds and thousands		D							

cont...

Information handling

DATA HANDLING	Collect	Organise	Display	Interpret
Watching TV				C, D
Yes or no?	B, C	B, C	B, C	B, C
My own chart	B, C	B, C, D	B, C, D	B, C, D
What colour is your car?				C, D
Pocket money			D	
Pie chart			D	
Averages				D, E
Computer database	D	D	D	D
Possibly, maybe				
How likely?				
What's the chance?				
In the bag				
Two coins				

Shape, position and movement

SHAPE AND SPACE	Range of shapes	Position & movement	Symmetry	Angle	Measure & estimate	Perimeter, formulae, scales
2D shapes	B, C, D					
Sort the shapes 1	C, D					
Drawing straws	C, D					
What's it called?	B, C, D					
True or false?			D	D		
3D shapes	D					
Sort the shapes 2	D					
Shape designs	C, D					
What's in a name?	D, E					
Describe the shapes	C, D					
Draw the shape	C, D					
Mirror symmetry			C, D			
Lines of symmetry			C, D			
Rotational symmetry			D, E			
Angle 1				C, D		
Angle 2				D, E		
Angle 3				D, E		
Nets of shapes	D					
Area and perimeter					D	D
Same area, different shape					D	E
Enlargement		D				E

Number, money and measurement

MEASURING	Measure & estimate	Time
How do you measure it?	B, C	
How long are your leaves?	B, C	
Measuring around	B, C	
Circles	C	
Scale drawing	D, E	
Surface area	C, D	
Volume and surface area	C, D	
How much is in the jug?	D	
What order?	D	
Weighing out the potatoes	C, D	
Is it true?	D	
Which is greater?	D	
Catching the bus		C, D
Catching the train		D
Time to investigate		D

NORTHERN IRELAND CURRICULUM FOR MATHEMATICS (KEY STAGE 2)

This grid indicates links between the activities and the relevant sections of the Programmes of Study. For each activity, reference is made to links with 'Processes in mathematics' and the appropriate content areas.

| | Processes in mathematics | | | Number | | | |
NUMBER	Using mathematics	Communicating mathematically	Mathematical reasoning	Understanding number & number notation	Patterns, relationships & sequences in number	Operations & their applications	Money
Number chains	d		a	a	a		
The morning post		d	f	a			
Quick off the grid 1	f			a	a		
Quick off the grid 2	f			a	a		
Which is closer? 1		a		c			
Which is closer? 2		a		c			
Jumping in tens	f		a	a	a		
Adding fives			f, a		a		
Spot the pattern			f, a		a		
All in order	d			a			
Addition grid			a, e			a, b	
Missing numbers	e		f			a, b	
Pick and mix	b	c			a		
Target 10	e		a, e			a	
Target 20	e		a, e			a	
Target 100 (a)			b, f	a		a	
Target 100 (b)			b, f	a		a	
Target 100 (c)	f, b		c			a	
Triple bonds	e, f		a			a	
Age gap	f			c		a	
In my head 1					a	a	
Explaining how you did it 1		c, e, f			a	a	
Taking away		c				a	
What's the difference? 1	e					a	
What's the difference? 2	e					a	
What's the difference? 3	e					a	
What's the difference? 4	e					a	
What's the difference? 5	e					a	
Countdown to zero			f	a			
Keep on adding	b					b	
Find the product 1		d				a	
Find the product 2		d				a	
Testing times! 1		d	c			a	
Testing times! 2		d	c			a	
Testing times! 3	d, e					a	
Number bugs	b				b	a	
Perfect bugs	b				b	a	
Puzzling times		c	a			a	
Square numbers 1	b	a	a		b		
Square numbers 2	b, e			b	b	b	
Cube numbers	f				b		
Keep on taking away	f					b	
Mix and match	f					b	
Explaining how you did it 2	e, f	c				a	
Division One	b					a	
Premier Division	b					a	
Find four facts	d					a, b	
Fill in the gaps		a				a	
In my head 2		d				a	
In my head 3		d				a	
Blank cheques 1		a					a
Blank cheques 2		a					a
European survey	b						a, b
Below zero		d	f			a	
Real numbers			f	c			
Fractions 1	b			d			
Fractions 2	e			d			
Fractions 3	e			d			
Fractions 4	b			d			
Percentages	b		f	d			
Spot the pattern			a	a	a		
What did I do?			a		c	a	
What comes later?			a		a, c		
Spot the rule			a, d		a	a	
Double trouble	f			a			
Input, output 1		d			c		
Input, output 2		d			c		
Input, output 3		d			c		
Trampoline party	d					b	
A sound deal	e						a
Shopper's choice	f						a
Find it!	f			c		b	
Round the block			d, e		c, d		
Nearest numbers	e, f					b	
Hundreds and thousands	b		f	b			c

cont...

CURRICULUM LINKS CHARTS

Processes in mathematics — Handling data

DATA HANDLING	Using mathematics	Communicating mathematically	Mathematical reasoning	Collect, represent & interpret data	Introduction to probability
Watching TV	b, c	c		a, c	
Yes or no?	c	d	e	a, b, e	
My own chart	c	d		a, b	
What colour is your car?	c	b		b, c	
Pocket money	b	b		c	
Pie chart	b	d		b	
Averages	b	a		f	
Computer database	d	d	e	e	
Possibly, maybe		a			a, b
How likely?		a	e		c
What's the chance?	b		c		c
In the bag	c	a	a		c
Two coins		a	a, c		c

Processes in mathematics — Shape and space

SHAPE AND SPACE	Using mathematics	Communicating mathematically	Mathematical reasoning	Exploration of shape	Position, movement & direction	Measures
2D shapes		a		a, c		
Sort the shapes 1	d			a		
Drawing straws	d	d		a		
What's it called?		a		a		
True or false?	b	a		a		
3D shapes		a	a, d	a, c		
Sort the shapes 2	d			b		
Shape designs		a, c		b		
What's in a name?		a	a, e	b, c		
Describe the shapes		a		a, b, c		
Draw the shape	b	a		a, b, c		
Mirror symmetry	a, d		c	a		
Lines of symmetry	a			a		
Rotational symmetry	a, e			a		
Angle 1	a	a			b, c	
Angle 2	a, b		a, d, e	c	a, d, f	
Angle 3		d	a, c	c	d	
Nets of shapes	d	d		b		
Area and perimeter	d	d	a, d, e	a		h
Same area, different shape	e		b	a		h
Enlargement		d	a, d, e	a	e	i

Processes in mathematics — Measures

MEASURING	Using mathematics	Communicating mathematically	Mathematical reasoning	Measures
How do you measure it?	b	a		b, d
How long are your leaves?	b			a, d
Measuring around	b			a, d
Circles	b		a, e	c, d, h
Scale drawing	a, b, f			d, i
Surface area		d	e	h
Volume and surface area	d	d		h
How much is in the jug?	b			b, d
What order?	a, b			d
Weighing out the potatoes	b			a, b
Is it true?	b, f	a		b, e
Which is greater?		a	c, f	f
Catching the bus	f			k
Catching the train	d			k
Time to investigate	e, f			l